MATHEMATICS
A NEW APPROACH

★

TEACHERS' BOOK 4

By D. E. Mansfield and M. Bruckheimer

★

MATHEMATICS: A NEW APPROACH

Pupils' Book 4

BACKGROUND TO SET AND
GROUP THEORY

including applications in the teaching of mathematics

By D. E. Mansfield and D. Thompson

MATHEMATICS: A NEW APPROACH

Pupils' Book 1   Teachers' Book 1
Pupils' Book 2   Teachers' Book 2
Pupils' Book 3   Teachers' Book 3

MATHEMATICS
A New Approach

D. E. MANSFIELD

Nuffield Mathematics Project
formerly Head of Mathematics Department
Holloway School

M. BRUCKHEIMER

Northampton College of
Advanced Technology, London

TEACHERS' BOOK 4

1965
CHATTO AND WINDUS
LONDON

Published by
Chatto & Windus (Educational) Ltd
42 William IV Street
London WC2

★

Clarke, Irwin & Co Ltd
Toronto

Printed in Great Britain by
Butler & Tanner Ltd
Frome and London

CONTENTS

PREFACE

THE present approach to the teaching of mathematics differs from the past approach in that it is simpler, in the sense that it uses fewer basic ideas, and broader based, in the sense that it applies these ideas to a wider range of activities, both practical and intellectual. It appears that, for these very reasons, it is easier for *children* to understand and use. Unfortunately, it is not usually easier for the *teacher* to understand, because most teachers are strongly inhibited by their training and experience. Any reasonably concise text which seriously attempts to present the more modern point of view must make great demands upon the teacher's willingness, patience and intellectual flexibility, at least within any educational system where the teacher plays a crucial part. It might perhaps be possible to minimise the importance of the teacher by producing extremely long texts wherein each sentence of explanation is followed by dozens of exercises: in practice, such courses tend to be extremely dull and, further, to induce once again the habit of mechanical rote-learning without understanding. Another possibility is a series of texts which deal with the newer topics in the old way, using the old ideas rather than the new. This, while creating interest, does not usually increase understanding even of the old ideas.

It seems once again that, in the long run, there is no easy road for the teacher: if he wishes to present his pupils with a modern approach to mathematics then he will have to exert himself far more than his pupils. He will have to discard some of his existing ideas, assimilate the new ones in spite of their strangeness and be prepared to explain to his pupils any points that they may find difficult. At the present time, when teachers are underprivileged and coping with oversized classes, this is undoubtedly hard. The alternative, of course, is to carry on as before. Let us not pretend to be teaching modern mathematics just because some lessons on sets or matrices are in our syllabus: if we, or our pupils, do not understand the underlying structural and mathematical reasons for the presence of such topics as these, then we are doing no more than replace the old dogma by a new one—and that is not worth doing.

Books 4 and 5 are a continuation up to G.C.E. O level of the basic

7

course provided in Books 1, 2 and 3. Because Books 4 and 5 are intended as an examination course there is a serious change in emphasis. In the first place they are being written for the more 'academic' type of pupil, whereas the first three books presented a basic course for pupils over a much wider range of ability. Secondly, we have included many more exercises in the text of the Class Book and further miscellaneous exercises at the ends of certain chapters. We may still not have included as many questions as in more standard texts: this is because it is intended that *all* the questions in each exercise should be worked (some demand a lot of the pupil), whereas in more standard texts most of the exercises were meant for 'drill' and the students were never expected to work them all. Here only the miscellaneous exercises are meant for revision and *further* practice: it is to be expected that the teachers will supplement these from the past papers of the examination which his pupils are sitting. The average O level candidate will probably need two years after completing Book 3 in order to complete Books 4 and 5: *very able* pupils may cover both the latter books in one year.

In consequence of the above, the form of the Teachers' Book is slightly altered. There are no further exercises: all exercises are now put in the Class Book. Also the notes on the text of the Class Book and the answers to the exercises are now given together in the order in which they appear in the Class Book: this is because we are often trying to make the pupil see or discover a particular point and we comment on this in the Teachers' Book. Answers to some of the more involved questions often include some working and details of solution. The answers given to these questions in the miscellaneous exercises taken from examination papers are those published by the respective examination boards where such answers are available. We should like to thank these boards for allowing us to use their questions. Our other answers have usually been calculated using four-figure logarithm tables where necessary (both three- and four-figure tables are in use for examination purposes), and some discrepancies may occur if tables with a different accuracy are used.

Regarding every separate G.C.E. O level syllabus in mathematics as a set of topics, then, say ten years ago, the difference between the union of all of them and the intersection of any two of them was a set containing only a few elements. Nowadays, the situation is rather different: the union of all the syllabuses contains far more elements than it did before, and the difference between this union and the intersection of any two syllabuses may also be larger.

Fortunately for the authors of these books, the many new elements appear to have been chosen as particular examples of a few mathematical ideas (and these ideas are common to many syllabuses although they are often not specifically mentioned in any particular syllabus); hence by treating these basic ideas themselves and then developing the new elements as examples of them, the authors hope to have provided a course suitable for almost any O level syllabus existing at the date of writing. (For exceptions see below.) Candidates whose syllabuses do not require knowledge of particular topics can omit the examples dealing with those topics, for many of the chapters and topics in the two books are independent of one another. In fact, the authors would deprecate this procedure on the grounds, first, that there is no particular reason to believe the old saw about quarts and pint pots has validity when applied to intellectual capacity, and, second, that there *is* reason to believe that a basic concept is formed and grasped more readily by considering a multitude of instances than by considering a single application.

It remains to be observed, so far as a few of the newer introductions to the syllabus are concerned, that generally acceptable conventions in respect of terminology, notation and symbolism have not yet become established. It is advisable, therefore, to obtain information about this from the syllabus (and, if possible, the most recent past papers) of the particular examining body chosen. We have tried to give as many common alternative notations and terms as we can: the alternatives are usually indicated in the Teachers' Book.

Exceptional syllabuses: These books do not attempt to cover such a geometry syllabus as the London Alternative 'A' Geometry; nor, regrettably, would they be adequate for an O level Statistics paper.

It is a pleasure to acknowledge gratefully the help of Norman Gowar, who corrected many details and checked the answers, and Maud Murphy for her competent work in producing the typescript from the scraps of paper on which both authors had scribbled.

CHAPTER ONE

Mappings

GENERAL NOTES

THE idea of 'functional relation' has always caused difficulties in mathematics – and the traditional notation has not helped. To write

$$y = x^2$$

and to claim that the inverse, depending on circumstances, is either

$$y = \sqrt{x} \quad \text{or} \quad x = \sqrt{y} \text{ (which are plainly different)}$$

(while usually being initially rather vague about whether $\sqrt{x}$ is to be single or double valued) is not a good start.

The fact is that the idea is simple, but not really quite as simple as the traditional approach makes it appear. Under the traditional approach the difficulties could hardly be stated, let alone explained. In the same sort of way the traditional notation was perhaps *too* good: if one understood the subject the notation was concise and suggestive, but if one did not understand the subject then the notation was no help, in fact, could even seem to direct one into error. For instance the use of $f(x)$ for both the function and the image of x is an admissible abuse if understood, but this is rarely the case.

One way to remove some of the difficulties is to look at the matter somewhat more generally and to clarify it by classification. If any sort of correspondence can be set up between the elements of one set and the elements of another, then that correspondence itself can be called a mapping from one set to the other. If, as in the text, we name the two sets domain and range, classify the mappings as many-many, many-one, one-many and one-one, and further classify them as 'into' or 'onto' mappings, then we have covered all the possibilities with which we are concerned. Many authors reserve the name 'mapping' for the many-one and one-one cases, and thus make it synonymous with 'function' (see note to Pupils' Book, page 11). We do not wish to do this, partly because it seems uneconomic to have two words for the same thing, and partly because we would dislike some of the consequences: for example, that the inverse of the mapping $x \rightarrow \sin x$ would not be a mapping at all. We try to avoid unnecessary artificialities: surely it is better to say that the inverse of a mapping is always a mapping, but that what *kind* of a mapping it is always needs to be investigated. If, also, we use the 'arrow' notation, for example, $f : x \rightarrow x^2$ which can be read as 'under the mapping f, the image of x is x^2', we focus the pupils' attention upon the mapping, rather than upon the image. We can easily combine mappings in suitable cases so that if

$$f : x \rightarrow x^2$$
$$\text{and } g : x \rightarrow 2x$$

we see clearly that
$$g \circ f : x \rightarrow 2x^2.$$
and
$$f \circ g : x \rightarrow 4x^2$$

(Notice that we work from right to left, as usual.)

It follows, of course, that we can decompose mappings into simple mappings. The particular mapping, called the identity mapping, $e : x \rightarrow x$ is very obvious and in the case of the inverse $\tilde{f}$ of a one-one mapping f we have $f \circ \tilde{f} = \tilde{f} \circ f = e$.

Diagrammatic representations of mappings may be found useful. Some examples follow.

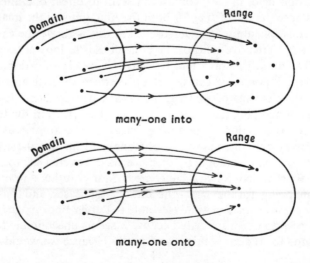

many–one into

many–one onto

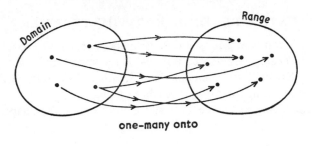

one-many onto

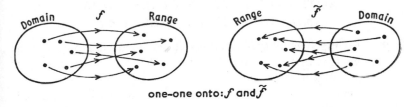

one-one onto: f and $\tilde{f}$

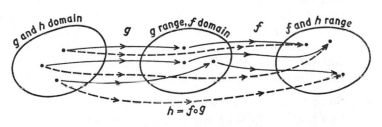

$h = f \circ g$

$h = f \circ g$ is shown dotted

One of the crucial points in this very important topic arises from the ambiguity of one-many mappings (these used to be called 'many-valued functions' but in fact some modern authors deny the name of 'function' to such a mapping). Using the classification and notation suggested and the precision they make available we can often find ways (usually involving equivalence relations) to remove the ambiguity and at the same time to remove the appearance of arbitrariness in some of the conventions which used to be established for the same purpose.

EXTRA READING FOR THE TEACHER

Chapters 3 and 4 of Mansfield & Bruckheimer: *Background to Set and Group Theory* (Chatto & Windus) is recommended.

Selby and Sweet: *Sets, Functions and Relations* (McGraw-Hill) contains an enormous quantity of teaching material.

On functional notation see Menger: *Calculus* (Ginn), Chapter 4.

NOTES ON TEXT OF CLASS BOOK
AND ANSWERS TO EXERCISES

p. 9   An approach like that outlined in the 'General Notes' and in the text makes phrases like 'find a formula' and 'changing the subject of a formula' more or less obsolete: nevertheless, some current syllabuses still use these phrases. It is suggested that the 'mapping' approach should be used even if the chosen syllabus does not specifically demand it, for it will be found that the degree of understanding obtained is greater; at the same time such topics as those just mentioned, together with their traditional notation, can be dealt with, if required, as in the text, as relative trivialities.

p. 9   Some other ways of illustrating the mapping are, for example, by a graph (see Pupils' Book, page 17), or a bar chart shown below: there are others.

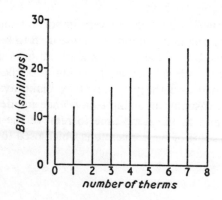

Exercise 1a Answer

$$
\begin{array}{ccc}
f & & g \\
10 \leftarrow & 0 \rightarrow & 30 \\
30 \leftarrow & 10 \rightarrow & 45 \\
50 \leftarrow & 20 \rightarrow & 60 \\
70 \leftarrow & 30 \rightarrow & 75 \\
90 \leftarrow & 40 \rightarrow & 90 \\
110 \leftarrow & 50 \rightarrow & 105 \\
130 \leftarrow & 60 \rightarrow & 120 \\
\end{array}
$$

$f\cdot 50 \rightarrow 110$, $g: 50 \rightarrow 105$. Hence the g mapping would be chosen.

* * * * *

p. 10   It is necessary that every element of the domain should have an image.

p. 11   Mapping the square natural numbers to their square roots,

$$4 \Big\langle \begin{array}{c} +2 \\ -2. \end{array}$$

p. 11   It is suggested that pupils should be encouraged to make up many non-mathematical examples of mappings of all types (one-one, many-one, one-many, many-many, into, onto) and classify them. The precise definition of domain and range in 'real-life' situations can lead to useful discussion.

If we are trying to be precise we naturally prefer to use 'onto' rather than 'into' mappings but it is not always convenient. For example, let the domain be the set of all telephone subscribers in London to-day. Let the range be the set of all possible four-digit numbers, 0000, 0001, 0002, . . . 9999. Then a mapping of each subscriber onto his number (ignoring his exchange), is, presumably, many-many into. If we keep the domain and mapping constant but ask for a precise listing of the elements of the onto range, then we have set ourselves a tedious (and probably useless) task. Note that it is still possible to define the 'onto' range precisely as the set of four-digit numbers in the directory. Incidentally, some authors use the word 'range' for what we have called the 'onto' range: others call it the 'strict' range.

It should be noticed that in practice very many 'mathematical' mappings have as both domain and range the set of all real numbers, and it is common, in such cases, to omit the definition of domain and range. Even in other cases one is often left to define the domain and range from the context.

p. 11 It is becoming common practice to use the word 'function' for one-one and many-one mappings only. Since this usage is not universal and some authors still use such phrases as 'many-valued functions' (which, in the new use of the word 'function', is a contradiction in terms), the word is not used in this book. It is not necessary, of course: the more general 'mapping' is entirely adequate.

Exercise 1b Answers

1. (a) One-one. Into.
   (b) Many-one. Into.
   (c) Real numbers from -1 to $+1$. Many-one.
   (d) Angles from $-90°$ to $90°$ (*or* equivalence classes of all angles such that angle A is equivalent to angle B if sin A = sin B).
   (e) Positive real numbers *or* negative real numbers *or* equivalence classes of all reals such that p is related to q if $p^2 = q^2$.
   (f) All people. Many-one. Into.
   (g) All men. One-many. Onto.
   (h) 1. Many-one.
   (i) $180°$ (*or* π^c). Many-one.

As mentioned in the Pupils' Book some gaps can be filled in more than one way: we have given one of the possible answers. It is often profitable to discuss the different answers suggested, but where possible the pupils should be encouraged to find the onto range.

2. (a) $\{x : x \in R; -1 \leqslant x \leqslant 1\}$, $\{x : x \in R; 0 < x\}$,
   $\{x : x \in \text{Men}; x \text{ has a son}\}$.

(b)

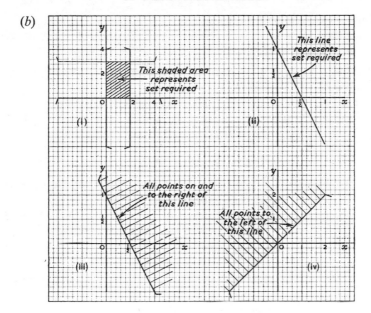

It should be mentioned that some authors prefer that areas required should be shaded *in*, while others have areas not required shaded *out*. There are various methods for indicating whether or not the boundary lines are to be included in the set.

3. (a) Many-one onto. (b) Many-one onto. (c) One-one onto.

4. It is not a mapping, for points on the equator have no images. Disregarding this, and using the term 'map' in the geographical sense, the set of points would form an unsatisfactory map, for the 'maps' of the north and south hemispheres would be superimposed on one another. The images of great circles (other than the equator) would be straight lines and the images of circles of latitude would be circles.

5. The onto range of $x \longrightarrow y$ is the set of natural numbers from 1 to 99 and zero.

(a) $x \longrightarrow x(100 - x)$: the onto range is $(1 \times 99, 2 \times 98, 3 \times 97,$ ... $100 \times 0)$: the into range could be more readily stated as the natural numbers less than 2501 (with zero).

(b) $x \longrightarrow x$. The onto range is A.

(c) $x \longrightarrow x^2 + (100 - x)^2$: the into range could be the natural numbers x such that $5000 \leqslant x \leqslant 10,000$.

6. The onto range is the set of all real numbers. The mapping is many-one.

   The 2×2 matrices which have no inverses map to zero.

   It is not true that every matrix whose image under d is 1 represents a shear translation.

* * * * *

p. 14 Combination and decomposition of mappings were mentioned in the general notes. They form a useful way of eliminating misunderstanding: for example, $\sin x^2$, $\sin {}^2x$ and $\sin (\sin x)$ can be clearly distinguished by decomposition. Machines (hand or electronic) perform calculations in this way. See Exercise 1c and also Chapter 7.

It may be observed that the symbol 'o' has been used to indicate the operation of combination of mappings.

Exercise 1c Answers

1. (a) (i) $x \longrightarrow x(x + 2) + 1 = x^2 + 2x + 1$
      (ii) $x \longrightarrow x(x + 1) + 2 = x^2 + x + 2$

   (b) (i) $x \longrightarrow x^2 + 1$
      (ii) $x \longrightarrow (x + 1)^2$.

2. (a) $x \longrightarrow x + 5 \longrightarrow x(x + 5) \longrightarrow x(x + 5) + 6$

   (b) $x \longrightarrow ax \longrightarrow ax + b \longrightarrow x(ax + b) \longrightarrow x(ax + b) + c$

   (c) $\left.\begin{array}{l} x \longrightarrow x^2 \\ x \longrightarrow \log x \end{array}\right\} \longrightarrow x^2 - \log x \longrightarrow x^2 - \log x - 9$

   (d) $\left.\begin{array}{l} x \longrightarrow \sin x \longrightarrow (\sin x)^2 \\ x \longrightarrow \cos x \longrightarrow (\cos x)^2 \end{array}\right\} \longrightarrow (\sin x)^2 + (\cos x)^2 = 1.$

3. Yes.

4. $g : x \longrightarrow 2x + 3$.

5. The neutral element is $x \longrightarrow x$.

   The inverse of $x \longrightarrow lx + m$ is $x \longrightarrow \dfrac{1}{l} x - \dfrac{m}{l}$.

The group is not commutative.

* * * * *

p. 15 With suitable pupils it can be made explicit that the inverse of the combination of two mappings is the combination of their inverses *in the reverse order*, i.e.

$$\overparen{(f \circ g)} = \tilde{g} \circ \tilde{f}.$$

For example, consider the following mappings:

$$a : x \longrightarrow 2x$$

$$\tilde{a} : x \longrightarrow \frac{x}{2}$$

$$b : x \longrightarrow x + 10$$
$$\tilde{b} : x \longrightarrow x - 10.$$

Then if f is, as before, $x \longrightarrow 10 + 2x$, we have

$$f = b \circ a \quad (\text{NOT } a \circ b).$$

Also, $\tilde{f}$, as in the text, is $x \longrightarrow \dfrac{x - 10}{2}$ and this decomposes

into $x \longrightarrow x - 10 \longrightarrow \dfrac{x - 10}{2}$. Thus

$$\tilde{f} = \tilde{a} \circ \tilde{b} \quad (\text{NOT } \tilde{b} \circ \tilde{a}).$$

p. 16 It should be obvious that $C = 10 + 2x$ is incorrect if C is regarded as cost and x as the number of therms used.

Exercise 1d Answers

1. (a) $x \longrightarrow x - 6$

   (b) $x \longrightarrow \dfrac{x + 3}{2}$

   (c) $x \longrightarrow \sqrt[3]{\dfrac{3x}{4\pi}}.$

2. (a) $x = \dfrac{5y + 58}{18}$

   (b) $x = \sqrt[5]{y} - 1.$

Exercise 1e Answers

(a) 70 shillings; (b) 35.

Exercise 1f Answers

1. The area is $16 + 16h$ square inches.

(a) $h \rightarrow 16 + 16h$. The inverse mapping is $h \rightarrow \dfrac{h - 16}{16}$

(b) (i) $A = 16 + 16h$

　(ii) $h = \dfrac{A - 16}{16}$.

(c)

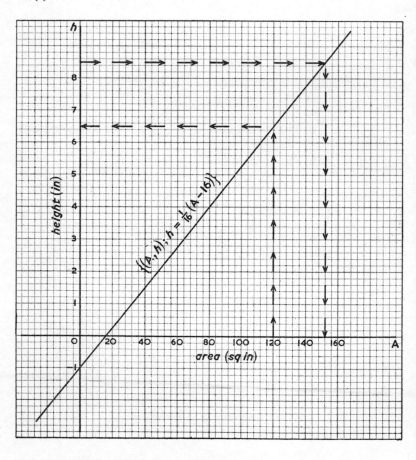

An area of 120 square inches corresponds to a height of $6\frac{1}{2}$ inches.

A height of $8\frac{1}{2}$ inches gives an area of 152 square inches.

2. (Note that there is a 'gap' in one of the axes.)

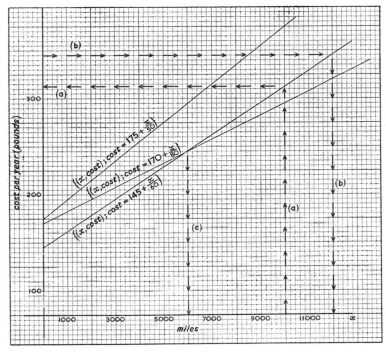

(a) £311 13s 4d

(b) 12,000 miles. 6·9 pence per mile

(c) 6000 miles

(d) No. The slope of the last graph is greater than the others and the cost when $x = 0$ is greater than for any of the others.

3. (a) $x \longrightarrow \pi x^2$ maps the radius of a circle to the area of the same circle.

$x \longrightarrow \sqrt{\dfrac{x}{\pi}}$ maps the area of a circle to the radius of the same circle.

(b) $A = \pi r^2$

$$r = \sqrt{\frac{A}{\pi}}$$

(c) $x \longrightarrow \frac{4}{3}\pi x^3$

$$x \longrightarrow \sqrt[3]{\frac{3x}{4\pi}}$$

(d) $r = \sqrt[3]{\frac{3V}{4\pi}}$

4. $x \longrightarrow \dfrac{x}{\pi r}$ gives no image for any value of x unless r is already known.

5. (a) $k = 8\frac{1}{2}$

   (b) π

   (c) $\dfrac{1}{\sqrt{\pi}}$

   (d) (i) $r = \sqrt{\dfrac{3V}{\pi h}}$

   (ii) 'the square root of the volume', 'the square root of the height', ' $\sqrt{\dfrac{3}{\pi}}$ '.

Other terminology is sometimes used: for example 'directly proportional', where we have used 'proportional'. The pupils' attention can be drawn to this as the need arises in any particular examination syllabus.

6. (a) 2

   (b) (i)

x	1	$2\frac{2}{3}$	4	16
y	$1\frac{1}{2}$	4	6	24

   (ii)

x	1	$2\sqrt{6}$	4	16
y	96	4	6	$\frac{3}{8}$

7. The constant of proportionality would be the uniform speed. The line passes through the origin because if $y = kx$ and $x = 0$ then $y = 0$.

(a) 'Best fitting' is not defined – as the matter stands one person might prefer one line and another another. This can lead on to a discussion of how the subjectivity could be replaced by mathematical objectivity, e.g. the method of least squares.

(b)

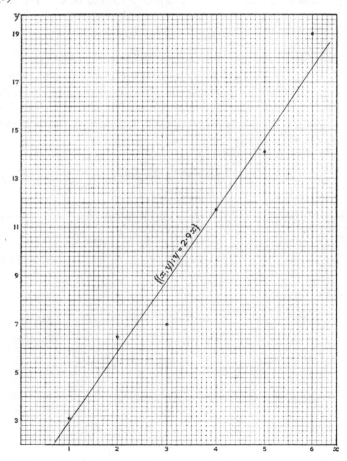

It is not to be expected that all members of a class will obtain the value given on the graph, $k = 2.9$.

(c) The scales should be such as to spread out the points concerned as far as possible. (With suitable pupils the point $\left(\dfrac{\Sigma x}{n}, \dfrac{\Sigma y}{n}\right)$ might be suggested.)

If it is found desirable the work may be extended as suggested in part (a) and by the consideration of other types of curves, e.g. $ax + b$ and ax^n, but probably Chapter 3 should be covered first.

8. 5.

* * * * *

pp. 23 to 24. This whole topic, using the idea of equivalence relations to justify what otherwise appear to be arbitrary conventions, is extremely important and should be thoroughly grasped. Many of the fundamental ideas of mathematics can be explained in terms of a limited number of ideas of which equivalence relation is one.

Exercise 1g Answers

1.

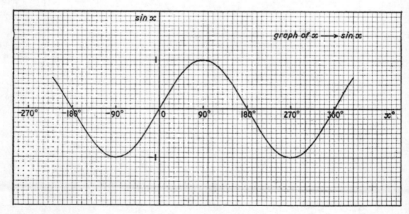

2. $d = 90°$

   (a) $-.6428$ (b) $-.7071$ (c) $.9397$ (d) $-.7660$ (e) $-.8660$.

3. (a) sin x   (b) − cos x   (c) − sin x   (d) cos x   (e) cos x
  (f) cos x   (g) sin x   (h) cos x.

4. (a) 15°   (b) 105°   (c) −15°   (d) 7°   (e) 90°
  (f) −90°   (g) 0   (h) 0   (i) 180°   (j) 90°.

5. (a) The set of real numbers x such that $-1 \leqslant x \leqslant 1$.
  (b) The domain is the set of real numbers x such that $-1 \leqslant x \leqslant 1$.

    The range is the set of x such that $-\dfrac{\pi}{2} \leqslant x \leqslant \dfrac{\pi}{2}$.

  (c) No.

SUGGESTIONS FOR FURTHER WORK

The way is plainly open here for work on periodic functions. It will probably be found that many pupils are interested in the relevant terminology of the electrical or radio engineer. It is also possible to begin to lay the foundations, by the 'addition' of curves, for Fourier analysis.

Odd and even functions are of considerable importance and could also be introduced here.

Also, some of the further work suggested in Exercise 1f, Number 7, may be found interesting.

CHAPTER TWO

Gradients

GENERAL NOTES

THIS chapter and the next contain a great deal of practical graphical work of a fairly traditional kind. The material is well known to be of considerable importance and no 'General Remarks' seem necessary. It may, perhaps, be mentioned that although in most examples the domain of the mapping is given, so that the numerical values to be covered by the axes can be deduced, no mention is made of the choice of scales. This perennial difficulty is thus left for the teacher to deal with.

The gradient of a mapping is a mapping, although we have chosen not to make this plain in the Class Book, preferring the usual approach via geometrical intuition at this stage.

NOTES ON TEXT OF CLASS BOOK AND ANSWERS TO EXERCISES

p. 27 The gradient of a graph or mapping at a point is stated as a number: any physical interpretation of it must be associated with the appropriate units.

Exercise 2a Answers

1. No answer required.
2. The gradient of both mappings is 4.
3. (*a*) —4   (*b*) 2   (*c*) 10   (*d*) *b*.

Exercise 2b Answers

(*a*) 9 ft per sec   (*b*) 7 ft per sec   (*c*) 5 ft per sec   (*d*) 4½ ft per sec
(*e*) 4·1 ft per sec   (*f*) 4·01 ft per sec   (*g*) 4·001 ft per sec.

The average speed comes closer and closer to *any* value equal to or less than 4 ft per sec as we decrease the time interval: but no matter how small a difference δ we choose, the average speed can be made to differ from 4 ft per sec by less than δ for all time intervals less than some interval determined by δ, and this is not true for any value other than 4 ft per sec.

*   *   *   *   *

p. 31   It may well be mentioned similarly that the gradient at a point of a mapping of time to speed gives a measure of the acceleration at the corresponding instant. Again, the gradient of a chord of such a graph measures the *average* acceleration over the time between the two corresponding instants.

p. 31   Just because a mapping gives an image for every x in the domain, it does not follow that a gradient exists at every point. Care must be taken to ensure that the mapping is *continuous* and has a unique gradient at the point considered. (This will be dealt with in Book 5. The meaning of 'continuous' has to be investigated carefully. For example, there are gaps between the stepping stones across a stream but they provide a continuous path provided one's stride is sufficiently long.) For example, in Book 3, Chapter 10 we saw that care had to be taken in the solution of an equation such

as $\dfrac{4}{x-2} - 2 = 0$. The mapping $x \to \dfrac{4}{x-2} - 2$ is usually

said to be discontinuous at $x = 2$ and the curve has no tangent at that point. Again, in the present chapter, as mentioned in Exercise 2c, Number 4, the mapping

$$\begin{cases} x \leqslant 40 & x \to 10 + 2x \\ x \geqslant 40 & x \to 30 + \dfrac{3}{2}x \end{cases}$$

is continuous at $x = 40$ but there is no single unique gradient at $x = 40$. This mapping is said to be continuous but non-differentiable at $x = 40$. (A mapping is said to be differentiable if the gradient mapping is many-one.)

Similarly, in Exercise 2c, Number 5, the graph of
$x \longrightarrow \tan x$ with domain $0° \leqslant x \leqslant 720°$ would show dis-
continuities at $90°$, $270°$, $450°$ and $630°$.

Exercise 2c Answers

1. $A = x^2$, $x = \sqrt{A}$.

x (units)	1	$1\frac{1}{2}$	2	$2\frac{1}{2}$	3	4
A $\binom{\text{square}}{\text{units}}$	1	$2\frac{1}{4}$	4	$6\frac{1}{4}$	9	16

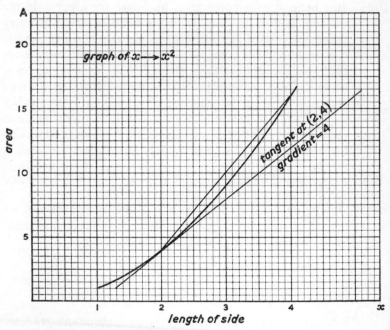

(*a*) (i) Gradient $= 6$.
    (ii) Over the range $x = 2$ to $x = 4$, the average increase in
area of the square is 6 square units per unit increase of x.

(b) (i) Gradient = $4\frac{1}{2}$.

  (ii) Over the range $x = 2$ to $x = 2\frac{1}{2}$, the average increase in
    area of the square is $4\frac{1}{2}$ square units per unit increase of x.

(c) Gradient of tangent at $x = 2$ is 4. When the length of the side
  reaches 2 units, the area of the square is increasing at the rate
  of 4 units of area per unit increase of the side.

2. To check Number 1 (b) (i) take $x_1 = 2$ and $h = \frac{1}{2}$.
  The gradient of the curve at $x = 2$ is 4.

3. (a) 4   (b) 4   (c) -4 (d) 8   (e) 5   (f) 10.

For Answer 4, see next page.

4.

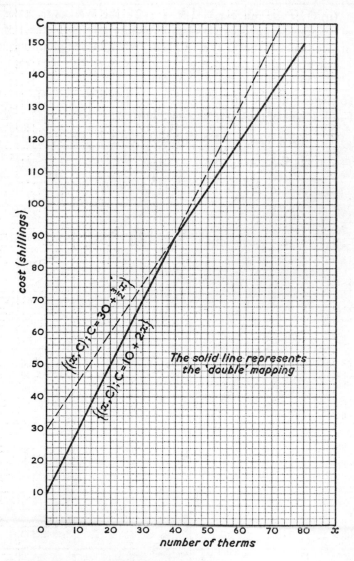

The gradient is undefined at $x = 40$.

5.

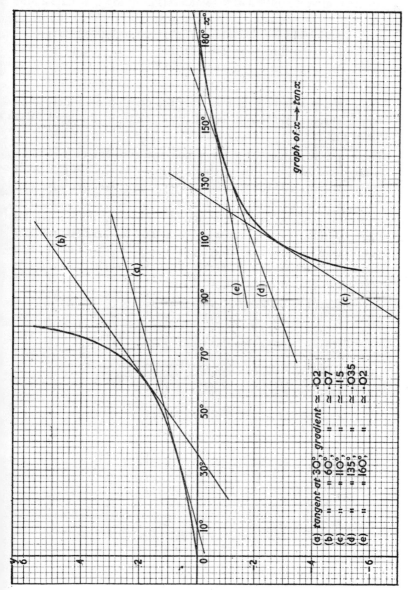

An alternative definition of $\theta \rightarrow \tan \theta$ is as follows: Rotate about O a radial line initially coinciding with Ox, through the given angle θ anticlockwise. Then $\tan \theta$ is the y co-ordinate of the point where the radial line intersects the line $x = 1$. (If a unit circle, centre the origin, is drawn the reason for the name '*tangent*' is evident.)

(Note: the gradients measured from the graph are unlikely to be very accurate: this should be used to point out the need for a better method.)

There are no values of x for which the gradient of $y = \tan x$ is negative. At $x = 0$ the gradient of $x \rightarrow \tan x$ is ·0175. As x increases from 80° towards 90°, $\tan x$ is positive and large and becomes rapidly greater and, given any number q, however large, a value of x can be found, less than 90°, such that $\tan x$ is greater than q. Similarly, as x decreases from 100° towards 90° $\tan x$ is negative and numerically large. Given any negative number n, a value of x can be found, greater than 90°, such that $\tan x$ is negative and numerically larger than n.

6. A convenient range is $-90° \leqslant x \leqslant 90°$.
   (*a*) $-85°$ (*b*) $82°$ (*c*) $0°$.

7.

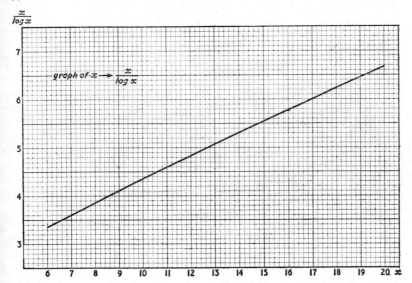

The graph of $x \to \dfrac{x}{\log x}$ is a smooth curve which differs from a straight line only very slightly in the neighbourhood of $x = 13$. At $x = 13$, the gradient is approximately ·24.

If the mapping gave the exact number of primes less than x, the gradient at $x = 13$ would mean that as x increased by 1 the number of primes would increase by ·24, or, roughly, that *in the neighbourhood of 13* there is about one prime to every four natural numbers.

The natural numbers near 13 are grouped in fours below and the primes are ringed. We see that this is a reasonable approximation.

$$8 \qquad 9 \qquad 10 \qquad \textcircled{11}$$

$$12 \qquad \textcircled{13} \qquad 14 \qquad 15$$

$$16 \qquad \textcircled{17} \qquad 18 \qquad \textcircled{19}$$

$$20 \qquad 21 \qquad 22 \qquad \textcircled{23}.$$

8.

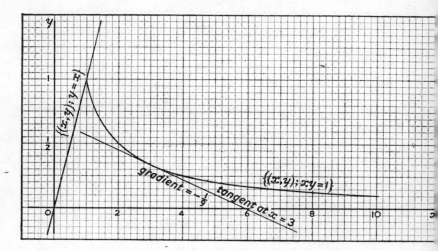

The graph of $y = \dfrac{1}{x}$ intersects the graph of $y = x$ at (1, 1) and (−1, −1).

At $x = 3$ the gradient of $y = \dfrac{1}{x}$ is $-\dfrac{1}{9}$ ($\simeq \cdot 11$)

.. $x = \frac{1}{3}$ ..   .. −9

.. $x = -\frac{1}{3}$ ..   .. −9

.. $x = -3$ ..   .. $-\dfrac{1}{9}$.

9.

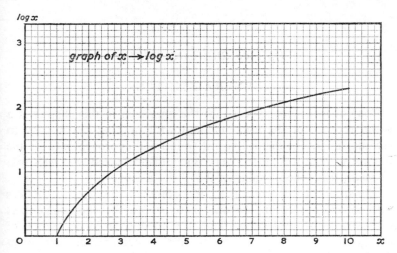

The onto range is the set of all real numbers from 0 to log 10,
i.e. 0 to 2·3026 approximately. (It is suggested that the teacher
should give the exact answers for (a) (b) (c) (d) before the class
attempts the rest of the questions.)

(a) 1   (b) 2   (c) 5   (d) 8½.

The significance is that the gradient of $x \rightarrow \log x$ appears to be
given by $\dfrac{1}{x}$ so that at the point where the gradient is $\dfrac{1}{20}$ it follows
that $x = 20$.

SUGGESTIONS FOR FURTHER WORK

It would be convenient and useful here to draw a few graphs of
trigonometric mappings, such as $x \rightarrow \sin x$, *with x in radians*, to
measure the gradients at various values of x, and to plot these
gradients against x. Pupils can then be brought to see that the
gradient of $\sin x$ is $\cos x$ and the gradient of $\cos x$ is $-\sin x$,
merely by bodily movement of the graphs. The fact that such relations do not hold if x is not measured in radians may help to reduce
the apparent antipathy towards circular measure.

CHAPTER THREE

Indices and Logarithms

GENERAL NOTES

IT may at first sight appear that the approach in this chapter is a wilful reversal of the usual method with nothing but novelty to recommend it. The fact is that the traditional approach to this topic has *not* worked well: it is a very rare student indeed who feels that he *understands* the meaning of $2 \cdot 8^{\sqrt 2}$ (let alone e^{π}).

The traditional approach, having obtained the rules for indices with natural number indices only, is to *assume* that these same rules will hold for all real indices and then to find an interpretation of fractional and negative indices to fit this assumption. This somewhat circular procedure cannot be extended to deal with all real indices and, furthermore, the pupil tends to disbelieve it: he mentally refuses to regard $2^{1 \cdot 23}$ as involving the 123rd power of the 100th root.

The approach in the text is to define a^x for real x as antilog $_a x$ and then to show, very simply, that such a definition conforms to the rules for indices when x is a natural number.

The accuracy of the class answers to the numerical exercises in this chapter will, of course, depend on the tables provided. Since many pupils will at this stage use a standard set of four figure tables, the answers in the Teachers' Book are given to the accuracy appropriate to four figure tables.

EXTRA READING FOR THE TEACHER

Allendoerfer and Oakley: *Principles of Mathematics* (McGraw-Hill) is recommended.

Exercise 3a Answers

(Note: It will probably be necessary to give advice about choice of scales.)

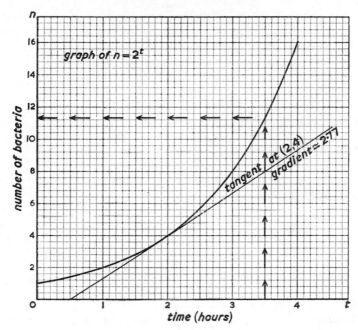

(a) 11   (b) approximately 2·77 bacteria per hour.

Exercise 3b Answers

1. (a) 3·078   (b) 4·292   (c) 3·653   (d) ·9001.
2. (a) 8·376   (b) 2·995.

*   *   *   *   *

p. 37   It should be pointed out again that logarithms to any base
establish an isomorphism between the positive real numbers
under multiplication and the real numbers under addition

$$x \times y = xy$$
$$\log x + \log y = \log xy$$

For further details about this section see Allendoerfer and
Oakley, op. cit.

The conversion of natural logarithms to common logarithms by division of all natural logarithms by the natural logarithm of 10 can, of course, be applied to the values of some natural logarithms obtained in Book 2.

Exercise 3c Answers

1. Note that it might be as well to discuss in advance the common error, when evaluating $\dfrac{\log_{10} x}{\log_{10} a}$, of calculating

$$\text{antilog } (\log_{10} x - \log_{10} a)$$

instead of

$$\text{antilog } \{\log (\log_{10} x) - \log (\log_{10} a)\}.$$

Further, difficulties may *seem* to arise if $\log_{10} x$ (or $\log_{10} a$) is negative, for we cannot then find $\log (\log_{10} x)$. There is, in fact, no difficulty: the quantity we require is $\dfrac{\log_{10} x}{\log_{10} a}$ and its magnitude can plainly be calculated by logarithms; its sign depends on the signs of numerator and denominator. For example, in (c) we have to evaluate $\dfrac{\log_{10} \cdot 6}{\log_{10} 3}$. Now $\log_{10} \cdot 6 \backsimeq \bar{1} \cdot 7782 = -\cdot 2218$, which is negative. All we have to do, therefore, is to evaluate

$$\frac{-\cdot 2218}{\log_{10} 3} \backsimeq - \frac{\cdot 2218}{\cdot 4771}$$

and $\dfrac{\cdot 2218}{\cdot 4771}$ can be calculated by logarithms in the usual way, the negative sign being attached afterwards.

(a) $1 \cdot 585$ (b) $\cdot 6310$ (c) $-\cdot 4648$ (or $\bar{1} \cdot 5352$)   (d) $\cdot 2623$ (using conversion via base 10, rather than using natural logarithm tables directly).

2. We have, using (3), $\log_b x = \dfrac{\log_{10} x}{\log_{10} b}$ and $\log_b a = \dfrac{\log_{10} a}{\log_{10} b}$

and so $\quad \dfrac{\log_b x}{\log_b a} = \dfrac{\log_{10} x}{\log_{10} b} \times \dfrac{\log_{10} b}{\log_{10} a} = \dfrac{\log_{10} x}{\log_{10} a}$

and this is $\log_a x$ (from (3)).

Using $\log_a b = \dfrac{1}{\log_b a}$ we should find that the answers to Number 1(a) and Number 1(b) are reciprocals, so that their product is 1, to the accuracy of the tables.

3. (a) 2   (b) 2   (c) −1 (or $\bar{1}$) (Note that $\log_{10} \dfrac{1}{10} = \dfrac{\log_b \frac{1}{10}}{\log_b 10}$ for any positive number b, using one of the results in Number 2. Hence

$$\log_{10} \frac{1}{10} = \frac{\log_b 1 - \log_b 10}{\log_b 10}.$$

But, from (3), $\log_b 1 = \dfrac{\log_{10} 1}{\log_{10} b} = 0$, and so $\log_{10} 1 = 0$ and $\log_{10} \frac{1}{10} = -1$.)
(d) −1 (or $\bar{1}$)   (e) $\frac{1}{3}$.

* * * * *

p. 39 It is convenient to represent the set of all positive real numbers by R^+. R^- and R are also used with the obvious interpretations.

p. 39 The point that (by (3) on Pupils' Book, page 38) $\log_a 1 = \dfrac{\log_{10} 1}{\log_{10} a} = 0$ should be made as often as possible. It follows from the definition of a^x as $\text{antilog}_a x$ that $a^0 = \text{antilog}_a 0 = 1$.

Exercise 3d Answers

1. (a) $10^1 \times 10^{.7} \simeq 10 \times 5{\cdot}012 = 50{\cdot}12$
   (b) $10^{2{\cdot}82} = 10^2 \times 10^{0{\cdot}82} \simeq 100 \times 6{\cdot}607 = 660{\cdot}7$
   (c) $10^{0{\cdot}26} \simeq 1{\cdot}820$
   (d) $10^{-0{\cdot}74} = 10^{\bar{1}{\cdot}26} = 10^{-1} \times 10^{0{\cdot}26} \simeq \frac{1}{10} \times 1{\cdot}820 = {\cdot}1820$
   (e) $10^{-1{\cdot}74} = 10^{-2} \times 10^{0{\cdot}26} \simeq \frac{1}{100} \times 1{\cdot}820 = {\cdot}0182$
   (f) $10^{-2{\cdot}06} = 10^{-3} \times 10^{0{\cdot}94} \simeq \frac{1}{1000} \times 8{\cdot}710 = {\cdot}00871$.

2. (a) $\log_{10} 5^{\frac{2}{3}} = \dfrac{\log_5 5^{\frac{2}{3}}}{\log_5 10} = \dfrac{\frac{2}{3}}{\log_5 10} = \frac{2}{3} \log_{10} 5 \simeq \frac{2}{3} \times {\cdot}699 = {\cdot}466$
   so $5^{\frac{2}{3}} \simeq 2{\cdot}924$.

(b) $\log_{10} 12^{2\frac{1}{2}} = 2\frac{1}{2} \times \log_{10} 12 \simeq 2\frac{1}{2} \times 1\cdot0792 = 2\cdot698$

so $12^{2\frac{1}{2}} \simeq 498\cdot9$.

(c) $\log_{10} 6^{12} = 12 \log_{10} 6 \simeq 9\cdot3384$

so $6^{12} \simeq 10^9 \times 2\cdot18$. (Find also the exact value! 2,176,782,336.)

(d) $\log_{10} 2^{3\cdot4} = 3\cdot4 \log_{10} 2 \simeq 1\cdot0234$

so $2^{3\cdot4} \simeq 10\cdot55$.

(e) $\log_{10} 3^{2\cdot5} = 2\cdot5 \log_{10} 3 \simeq 1\cdot1928$

so $3^{2\cdot5} \simeq 15\cdot59$.

(f) $\log_{10} 2\cdot8^{5\cdot2} = 5\cdot2 \log_{10} 2\cdot8 \simeq 2\cdot3254$

so $2\cdot8^{5\cdot2} \simeq 211\cdot5$.

(g) $\log_{10} e^{1\cdot411} = 1\cdot411 \log_{10} e \simeq \cdot6128$

so $e^{1\cdot41} \simeq 4\cdot101$.

(Alternatively, from the natural logarithm tables, $e^{1\cdot411} \simeq 4\cdot1$)

3. $\log_a b^x = \dfrac{\log_b b^x}{\log_b a} = \dfrac{x}{\log_b a} = x \log_a b.$

4. (a) The note on page 39 obtained

$$a^0 = 1 \text{ from } \log_a 1 = \frac{\log_{10} 1}{\log_{10} a} = 0$$

and from the definition $a^x = \text{antilog}_a x$.

The same result is *now* obtained from the induced rules for indices:

(i) $1 = \dfrac{a^m}{a^m} = a^0$ (ii) $\dfrac{a^m}{a^{m+2}} = \dfrac{1}{a^2} = a^{-2}$

(iii) $\dfrac{a^m}{a^{m+b}} = \dfrac{1}{a^b} = a^{-b}.$

(b) (i) $10^{1\cdot23} \simeq 16\cdot98$ (ii) $10^{-1\cdot74} = 10^{\bar{2}\cdot26} \simeq \cdot0182$

(iii) $\dfrac{2^0}{2^{-\cdot26}} = 2^{\cdot26} \simeq 1\cdot198$

(iv) $\log_{10} 3^{\cdot5} = \cdot5 \times \log_{10} 3 \simeq \cdot2386$

$\log_{10} 2^{1\cdot6} = 1\cdot6 \times \log_{10} 2 \simeq \cdot4816$

$\log_{10} (3^{\cdot5} \div 2^{1\cdot6}) \simeq \cdot2386 - \cdot4816 = \bar{1}\cdot757$

so $3^{\cdot5} \div 2^{1\cdot6} \simeq \cdot5715$.

(c) For $x > 0$ the result is already established. See part (a). The case $x = 0$ has been dealt with.

If $x < 0$, say $x = -b$, then $\dfrac{1}{a^x} = \dfrac{1}{a^{-b}}$ where $b > 0$.

Hence, by part (a), $\dfrac{1}{a^x} = \dfrac{1}{\dfrac{1}{a^b}} = a^b = a^{-x}$.

5. (a) 2   (b) 3.

Note: the examination syllabus may require further developments: e.g. evaluate $2^{-\frac{1}{2}}$; if so, a fair amount of practice may be necessary. Further, our mapping is one-one, and so $a^{\frac{1}{2}}$ can only have one value: some syllabuses require two. From our point of view this can be satisfactorily dealt with after the introduction of complex numbers.

6. The opportunity may be taken to clear up the confusion arising from the use of 'pyramidal' index notation: exponentiation is not associative, for $(a^b)^c \neq a^{(bc)}$. Thus, for example, 2^{3^2} is ambiguous: regarding it as $(2^3)^2 = 2^6$ we obtain 64, while, regarding it as $2^{(3^2)}$ we obtain 512.

(a) 9   (b) 27   (c) 1000   (d) 128.

* * * * *

p. 41   Observe, here and later, the 'gaps' in the axes of the graphs. In the graph on this page we must accept either that there is no point on the n-axis corresponding to n = 0 or that the vertical axis is broken.

pp. 41 et seq. The precise meaning of 'continuous' and 'discontinuous' will be investigated in Book 5. For the present the intuitive idea will serve.

Exercise 3e Answers

1. $A = 2 \times 3^t$

Area covered on 1 July 1975 (without chemical) would be $2 \times 3^{11.5} \simeq 613{,}600$ acres.

Area covered on 1 July 1975 (with chemical) will be

$$2 \times 3^3 \times (\tfrac{3}{2})^{8\frac{1}{2}} \simeq 1695 \text{ acres.}$$

2. (a)

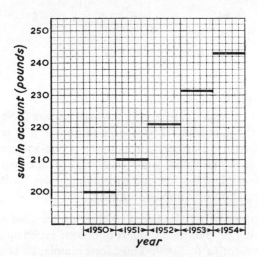

(b) £220 15s 3d (to nearest penny).

(c) $200 \times 1.05^{25} \approx 677.6$. Amount is £678 to the nearest pound. (It is unlikely that more than the first three figures are reliable.) $200 \times 1.0125^{100} \approx 693$. Amount is about £690.

(d) Amount after 25 years at 5% simple interest = £450. Difference = £227.

3. Gradient is 409·2. The average increase in the number of bacteria per hour from 2 p.m. to midnight is 409·2.

* * * * *

p. 46   The significance of the sign of the gradient should be pointed out.

Exercise 3f Answers

(a) $10^{-6} \approx 2^{-t}$ implies $10^{-6} \approx (10^{.3010})^{-t}$ implies $t \approx \dfrac{6}{.3010} \approx 20$.

The time is 20 hours (to the nearest hour).

(b) $m = 2^{-10} \approx .00098$ g (to 5 decimal places).

(c) Average loss in the hour following time $= t$ is $2^{-t} - 2^{-(t+1)}$

$= 2^{-(t+1)}$. Now $2^{-(t+1)} < 10^{-2}$ implies $(10^{\cdot3010})^{-(t+1)} < 10^{-2}$ from which $t > 5\cdot7$. Hence the first such hour is 6–7 p.m.

* * * * *

p. 47 The point here, and in Exercise 3g, arises from the fact that exponential mappings are extremely common and we need to devise a method (here found empirically) for calculating their gradients.

Exercise 3g Answers

1. (a)

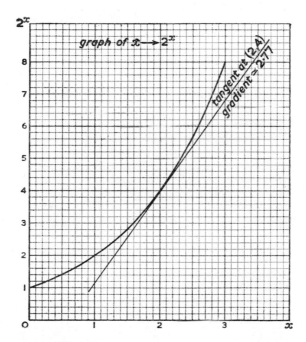

For Answer 1 (b), *see next page.*

(b)

(c)

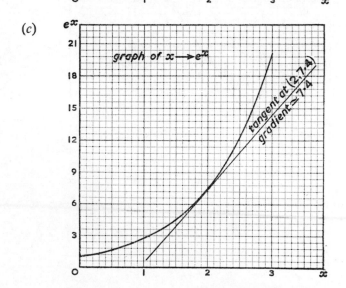

(*d*)   (This case is rather difficult to draw!)

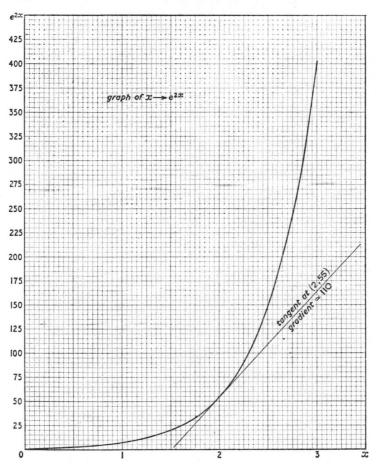

graph of $x \longrightarrow e^{2x}$

tangent at (2.55) gradient ≈ 110

We see that in (*c*) the gradient is numerically approximately equal to the y co-ordinate and that in (*d*) the gradient is numerically approximately equal to twice the y co-ordinate.

2. (*a*)

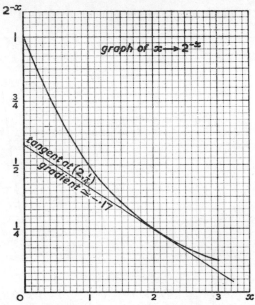

(*b*)

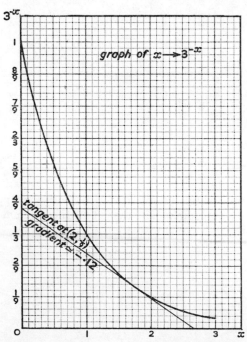

(c)

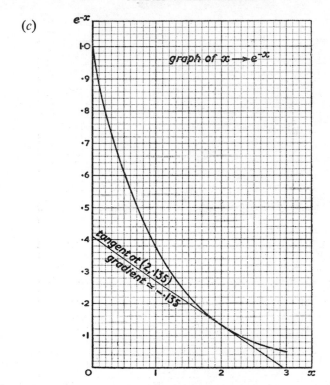

For Answer 2 (d), see next page.

(d)

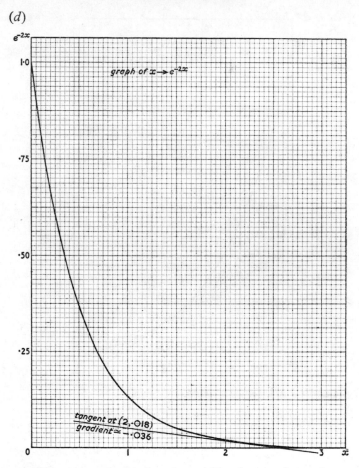

graph of $x \rightarrow e^{-2x}$

tangent at (2, ·018)
gradient ≈ — ·036

Here we see in (c) that the gradient is negative and numeric-ally equal to the y co-ordinate. In (d) the gradient is negative and numerically equal to twice the y co-ordinate.

* * * * *

p. 48   It now seems likely, but of course we have not 'proved', that the gradient of $y = e^{ax}$ is ae^{ax}, that is, ay. Practice is now needed in expressing relations of the form $y = p^{qx}$ in the form $y = e^{ax}$ so that this empirically discovered rule may be applied to find the appropriate gradients.

Exercise 3h Answers

1. $n = 2^t$ implies $n = (e^{\log 2})^t = e^{t \times \log 2}$.

   Hence the gradient is $\log 2 \times e^{t \times \log 2} = 2^t \times \log 2$.

   At $t = 5$ the gradient is $2^5 \times \log 2 \simeq 22 \cdot 18$.

   Thus, at 5 p.m., the number of bacteria is increasing by $22 \cdot 18$ per hour approximately.

2. $m = 2^{-t}$ implies $m = e^{-(\log 2)t} = e^{-t \times \log 2}$.

   Hence the gradient is $(-\log 2) \times e^{-t \times \log 2} = 2^{-t} \times (-\log 2)$.

   At $t = 10$ the gradient is $2^{-10} \times (-\log 2) \simeq -\dfrac{\cdot 6931}{1024} \simeq \cdot 00068$.

   Thus, at 10 p.m., the mass is decreasing by $\cdot 00068$ g per hour approximately.

MISCELLANEOUS EXERCISES I Answers

1. Greater than 1.
2. (a) (i) 3·141593   (ii) 3·142.
   (b) (i) 2   (ii) ± 7   (iii) ± $\frac{1}{8}$.
   (c) ± ·5719.

3. (i) 16s 8d, $1\frac{1}{9}$%   (ii) $\left(\dfrac{np - 95ct}{10}\right)$s.

4. £420 0s 6d.

5. (i) (a) 0   (b) ·064   (ii) $x = ±\ 1000$.

6. (i) $f = \dfrac{uv}{v - u}$ (ii) $1·92 \times 10^{13}$.

7. (i) $p = \frac{1}{2}$, $q = 3\frac{1}{3}$ (ii) 1·63   (iii) 8.

8. 3·6 in, $a = 1·2$, $b = 0·2$.

9. (i)

t	0	1	2	3	4	5
s	0	0·25	1·25	3	5·5	8·75

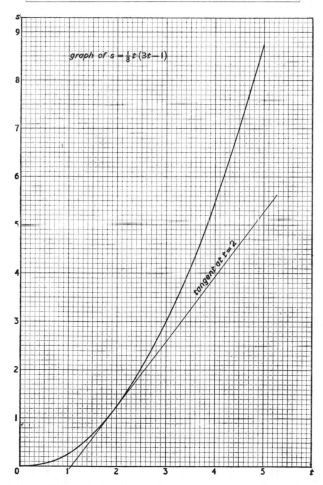

graph of $s = \frac{1}{8}t(3t-1)$

tangent at $t = 2$

(ii) (*a*) 2·125 units/sec   (*b*) 1·75 units/sec   (*c*) 1·56 units/sec
(iii) 1·38 units/sec.

10. $R = \dfrac{100}{T}\left(\dfrac{A}{P} - 1\right).$

11. (i) 11.15 a.m.
    (ii) 91,700.

12. (a) 2 ft/sec   (b) 0 ft/sec   (c) 4 ft/sec.

13. $x = y^2 - 4y, \quad x = 12.$

14. $x \rightarrow \dfrac{x^2}{a} - b.$

15. (a) 39° 32′, 320° 28′   (b) 59° 43′, 239° 43′.

16. (i) 96   (ii) $n = 3, K = 1{\cdot}6, x = 10, y = 345{\cdot}6.$

17. (ii) 26th week, £1,080.

18. $y = 12, x = 3\tfrac{1}{3}.$

19. (a) 1824 years   (b) (i) $\cdot$978 m_0 (ii) $\cdot$038 m_0 (iii) 0.

20. 1, 1·56.

21. (a) $R = 10$ (b) $r = \pm 2 \sqrt{\left(\dfrac{I}{M} - \dfrac{l^2}{12}\right)}.$

CHAPTER FOUR

Boolean Algebra and Sets

GENERAL NOTES

IN this chapter we introduce two new words in the language of sets and then develop the idea of a Boolean algebra. We have chosen to do this axiomatically, since if it is felt desirable to introduce the idea of axioms in school mathematics it is much more desirable to do it for an algebraic structure than for a geometry with all its intuitive overtones. As a motivation in choosing the axioms we use the idea of a field and the properties of set algebra with which we are already familiar.

Having used the algebra of sets to obtain the definition of an abstract Boolean algebra one might wonder whether in fact we have gained anything. We have certainly gained the advantage that abstraction always confers, that is, that we can discuss the system without confusing irrelevancies, and that we can more easily see which practical situations (other than sets) are models of the abstract system. But there is another possible interpretation of 'gain': is there an abstract Boolean algebra which cannot be represented by a set algebra? The answer to this is no: given any abstract Boolean algebra then it has been proved (by M. H. Stone in 1936) that there is always a universal set such that the algebra of the subsets is 'isomorphic' to the given abstract Boolean algebra. So in this sense we have gained nothing.

In the next chapter we discuss two applications of Boolean algebra which are of considerable consequence in the modern world. It might be advisable in the teaching situation to mention the two applications briefly before beginning the general discussion of this chapter, but we feel that subsequently the abstract algebra should be developed on its own. Then finally the abstract results obtained can be interpreted in their applications.

EXTRA READING FOR THE TEACHER

Allendoerfer and Oakley: *Principles of Mathematics* (McGraw-Hill), Chapters 1 and 13.
Birkhoff and Mac Lane: *Survey of Modern Algebra* (Macmillan), Chapter XI.

NOTES ON TEXT OF CLASS BOOK
AND ANSWERS TO EXERCISES

p. 54   The obvious symbol U is sometimes used for the universal set but tends to be confused with the symbol for union.

p. 54   Notice that, in the first example given, the universal set $\mathscr{E}$ has been chosen to avoid a difficulty: the number 1 is neither prime nor composite.

p. 55   Equations (1) and (2) are known as *de Morgan's Laws*.

Exercise 4b Answers

2. (a) $= A \cap B \cap C$ (b) $= A' \cap B \cap C$ (c) $= A \cap B' \cap C$
   (d) $= A \cap B \cap C'$ (e) $= A \cap B' \cap C'$ (f) $= A' \cap B \cap C'$
   (g) $= A' \cap B' \cap C'$ (h) $= A' \cap B' \cap C$.

3. (a) $(A \cap B' \cap C') \cup (A \cap B' \cap C)$
   (b) $(A \cap B \cap C) \cup (A \cap B \cap C')$
   (c) $(A' \cap B' \cap C') \cup (A' \cap B' \cap C)$.

The importance of canonical forms arises from the fact that every expression, no matter how complicated, can be expressed in canonical form in just *one* way (except for a possible rearrangement of 'factors'): hence if two complicated expressions both give rise to the same canonical form then they are identical, no matter how different they appear. Conversely, if two expressions which seem to mean the same thing give rise to different canonical forms, then they are in fact different. The reduction to canonical form can easily be performed by a machine, and this is in fact done, for instance, to ensure that the statement of the circumstances out of which an insurance claim arises matches up with the conditions, as stated on the insurance policy, under which insurance is payable. (See, also, the next chapter.)

Notice also that if we are dealing with expressions involving two sets only, then we can find canonical forms in two letters for all these expressions if we want to. For instance

$$A \triangle B = (A' \cap B) \cup (A \cap B').$$

* * * * *

p. 58 The subsequent development is desirable but not essential. It could be replaced by a thorough discussion of set algebra with more being made of points such as those mentioned in Exercise 4c Number 4. Then in the next chapter it could be shown that the two applications have similar structure to that of set algebra. But we repeat that we feel that it is desirable to treat the subject properly: it is not too difficult for the pupil if the teacher is at ease with the subject. It is certainly no more involved than the one-time geometric 'proofs'. It is important to keep the set algebra motivation in mind throughout and perhaps draw an occasional diagram.

A discussion based on the following points could precede that given in the Class Book.

In Chapter 9 of Book 3 we discussed various mathematical structures. Much basic mathematics is concerned with the investigation of sets with structure. The motivation to study any particular structure may come in two possible ways. In the first place we may already have been studying a structure and our considerations may lead us to modify the definitions: this is what we might call an internal motivation. The second possible motivation occurs when we come across an example whose underlying structure has not yet been studied abstractly: the example is often known as a 'model' of the abstract structure. For instance, the rational numbers under addition and multiplication are a 'model' (example, interpretation, realisation) of a field. We are now in the second position: a set of sets (contained in a universal set) under the

binary operations ∩, ∪ and the unary* operation ′ is not an
example of a known abstract structure so we shall set up such
an abstract structure, investigate its properties briefly and
then find other examples of it. In order to have some guidance
in the choice of definition of our new structure (after all we
could make the defining properties include all the properties
of sets that we know, but this would be uneconomical,
since some are deducible from others: the idea is always to
keep the required properties, as far as possible, to a minimum)
we shall compare the set structure with field structure.

p. 58   The use of o, □, a' and $\tilde{a}$ is preferable here to $+$, $\times$, $-a$ and
$\dfrac{1}{a}$ since we are going to compare set algebra with the field
structure. However, when considering fields in isolation the
latter notation can be justified, see Mansfield and Bruckheimer: *Background to Set and Group Theory* (Chatto and
Windus), Chapter 13, especially page 238.

p. 59   In property 5 we have to exclude O: it has no inverse for □,
i.e. it has no image under the unary operation ∼. This may
seem an arbitrary exclusion, but it can be shown (op. cit.,
p. 230) that property 6 is inconsistent with the inclusion of O.

p. 59   The fact that ∪ is distributive over ∩ is not deducible from
properties 1 to 6. This follows, for instance, from the fact
that rational numbers are an example of a field and addition
is not distributive over multiplication. The addition of property 6a and the modification of property 5 effectively 'sym-
metrise' the field, so obtaining the very important property of
duality discussed subsequently.

p. 60   Knowing the theorem proved by Stone, referred to in the
'General Notes', we realise that every model of a Boolean
algebra must satisfy the stated results for sets. Whether it
is desirable to quote this result at this stage is doubtful. In
any case, the pupil can learn a lot about 'proving' a result

---

*A *unary operation* is a mapping which associates with any element of a set
another unique element of the set. Thus in a group the mapping of an element
onto its inverse is a unary operation.

from a given set of axioms by working through the examples provided.

p. 60 Property 7 differs from the previous six in that we have deduced it from these six: the six themselves were just stated. We cannot ask whether they are true or false, only whether they are consistent (which they are; we have a model) or whether any of them are redundant. (We might distinguish by calling 7 a 'theorem'.) We could, of course, make 7 an axiom, but it would certainly have been redundant. In fact, there are redundancies in the set of axioms we have chosen, but this need not worry us seriously: we try to keep the number of axioms down but do not exert ourselves overmuch to obtain an ultimate minimum set.

An example of a redundancy is the statement at the end of axiom 5', viz 'a' is the only element which has these two properties for any a'. This can be derived from the other axioms, but the derivation is not important. (See Miscellaneous Exercises II, Number 4(b).)

Exercise 4c Answers

1. $\begin{aligned} a \square O &= O \circ (a \square O) & (4) \\ &= (a \square a') \circ (a \square O) & (5') \\ &= a \square (a' \circ O) & (6) \\ &= a \square a' & (4) \\ &= O & (5') \end{aligned}$

and $\begin{aligned} a \square a &= O \circ (a \square a) & (4) \\ &= (a \square a') \circ (a \square a) & (5') \\ &= a \square (a' \circ a) & (6) \\ &= a \square I & (5') \\ &= a & (4) \end{aligned}$

2. Axioms or results used at each step are respectively

$\qquad$ 6a, 3, 2, 5', 7 and 2, 8, and 2, 6, 3, 2, 5', 7 and 2, 8.

The result follows from axiom (5').

A possible proof of 9 is

$\qquad a \circ a = (a' \square a')'$ (11 with $b = a$)

whence $\qquad a = (a')'$.   (8)

A possible proof of 10 is
$$a \circ I' = (a' \,\square\, I)' \qquad \text{(11 with } b = I' \text{ and 9)}$$
$$= (a')' \qquad\qquad \text{(4)}$$
$$= a. \qquad\qquad\quad \text{(9)}$$

Since this is valid for all a and O is unique, hence by (4) $I' = O$. The second result follows by 'duality'.

3. The table for union is

A	B	A ∪ B
1	1	1
1	0	1
0	1	1
0	0	0

In order to show that the given structure is a Boolean algebra the six axioms have to be verified. The associative and distributive axioms need only be verified by taking a single example: it is too tedious to go through all possibilities.

4. (a) (i) The table is

A	B	C	B ∪ C	A ∩ (B ∪ C)	A ∩ B	A ∩ C	(A ∩ B) ∪ (A ∩ C)
1	1	1	1	1	1	1	1
1	1	0	1	1	1	0	1
1	0	1	1	1	0	1	1
0	1	1	1	0	0	0	0
1	0	0	0	0	0	0	0
0	1	0	1	0	0	0	0
0	0	1	1	0	0	0	0
0	0	0	0	0	0	0	0

Since columns 5 and 8 are the same the result is proved.

(*a*) (ii) The table is

A B	A ∪ B	(A ∪ B)′	A′	A′ ∩ B	(A ∪ B)′ ∪ (A′ ∩ B)
1 1	1	0	0	0	0
1 0	1	0	0	0	0
0 1	1	0	1	1	1
0 0	0	1	1	0	1

Since columns 5 and 7 are the same the result is proved.

(*b*) The table for △ is

A B	A △ B
1 1	0
1 0	1
0 1	1
0 0	0

The fact that △ is associative follows from the following table; columns 5 and 7 are the same.

A B C	A △ B	(A △ B) △ C	B △ C	A △ (B △ C)
1 1 1	0	1	0	1
1 1 0	0	0	1	0
1 0 1	1	0	1	0
0 1 1	1	0	0	0
1 0 0	1	1	0	1
0 1 0	1	1	1	1
0 0 1	0	1	1	1
0 0 0	0	0	0	0

5. The tables for the □ and ' operations are

□	1	3	5	15
1	1	1	1	1
3	1	3	1	3
5	1	1	5	5
15	1	3	5	15

'	
1	15
3	5
5	3
15	1

In the verification it should be found that 'O' $= 1$, 'I' $= 15$. The structure for $\mathscr{E}_4$ is not a Boolean algebra. For instance

$$2 \circ 2' = 2 \circ 2 = 2$$

and 2 is not I, which violates 5'.

The structure for $\mathscr{E}_6$ is a Boolean algebra isomorphic to the structure for $\mathscr{E}_{15}$. The tables are

o	1	2	3	6
1	1	2	3	6
2	2	2	6	6
3	3	6	3	6
6	6	6	6	6

□	1	2	3	6
1	1	1	1	1
2	1	2	1	2
3	1	1	3	3
6	1	2	3	6

'	
1	6
2	3
3	2
6	1

If the table

o	O	a	a'	I
O				
a				
a'				
I				

is completed using the axioms and results proved for a Boolean algebra, it will be found that it can be completed in only one way. Hence if any structure on a set of four elements has different combination tables (i.e. is non-isomorphic to this structure) it cannot be a Boolean algebra.

$\mathscr{E}_{27}$ does not have the structure of a Boolean algebra: consider the half-completed table

o	1	3	9	27
1	1	3	9	27
3	3	3	9	27
9				
27				

It should be clear that if a natural number p has repeated factors it does not give rise to a Boolean algebra.

6.
$$A \triangle B = (A \cap B') \cup (A' \cap B)$$
$$A \circledast B = (A \cup B') \cap (A' \cup B).$$

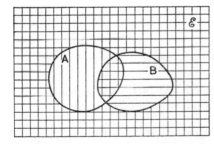

A ∪ B′ shaded vertically
A′ ∪ B shaded horizontally
A ⊛ B shaded both ways

The set of all subsets of some set $\mathscr{E}$ with binary operation ⊛ is a group. The identity is $\mathscr{E}$ and the inverse of any set A is A itself.

CHAPTER FIVE

Logic and Switching Circuits

GENERAL NOTES

IN this chapter we consider two examples of a Boolean algebra which have considerable practical importance. We do not directly establish either system as a Boolean algebra but apply the '(0,1)' algebra of Exercise 4c Number 3: in the notes we shall explain more fully how the former could be done.

EXTRA READING FOR THE TEACHER

Allendoerfer and Oakley: *Principles of Mathematics* (McGraw-Hill), Chapters 1 and 13.
Birkhoff and Mac Lane: *Survey of Modern Algebra* (Macmillan), Chapter XI.
D. E. Rutherford: *Introduction to Lattice Theory* (Oliver and Boyd).

NOTES ON TEXT OF CLASS BOOK AND ANSWERS TO EXERCISES

p. 66   Instead of a' many authors use $\sim a$. Also instead of using 0 and 1 in the tables, F and T are often used. Notice that we use $\Leftrightarrow$ and not $=$ since we are discussing the logical equivalence of statements. We explain this in detail in the next note and that to pages 71–72.

p. 67   In order to give the set of statements itself a Boolean structure we could introduce a true statement t and a false statement f, which would remain fixed in any discussion. This compares with choosing a fixed universal set and a fixed null set in the discussion of any set problems and just as there we do not need to be explicit about the choice, so here we have no need to do so. The statement t corresponds to I and f to O in the abstract Boolean algebra.

A much more satisfactory approach is to use the idea of equivalence classes. Consider, say,

$$a \wedge (b \wedge c) \Leftrightarrow (a \wedge b) \wedge c:$$

the $\Leftrightarrow$ is used to mean that the two expressions are logically equivalent whatever a, b or c. It is in fact itself a statement which is always true. The relation $\Leftrightarrow$ is an equivalence relation in the set of statements and we can form the equivalence classes. Denote the equivalence class to which a statement a belongs by $\{a\}$. Then it is easily shown that

(i) if $a \Leftrightarrow b$ and $c \Leftrightarrow d$ then $a \wedge c \Leftrightarrow b \wedge d$
    and $a \vee c \Leftrightarrow b \vee d$;

(ii) if $a \Leftrightarrow b$ then $a' \Leftrightarrow b'$,

Hence we can define (iii) $\{a\} \wedge \{b\}$ to be $\{a \wedge b\}$,

(iv) $\{a\} \vee \{b\}$ to be $\{a \vee b\}$,

and (v) $\{a\}'$ to be $\{a'\}$.

By $\{a\} = \{b\}$ we would mean that $\{a\}$ is the same set of statements as $\{b\}$, i.e. $\{a\}$ and $\{b\}$ are the same equivalence classes and a is logically equivalent to b. If now we denote the equivalence class of all statements which are always true (tautologies like $a \vee a'$, see Example 2, page 70) by t and the equivalence class of all statements which are always false (self-contradictions like $a \wedge a'$, see Example 4, page 72) by f, then the set of equivalence classes of statements has the structure of a Boolean algebra with t as the I element and f as the O element.

The reader who is unfamiliar with the basic concepts of this approach will find a discussion of the interaction of binary operations and equivalence relations in Chapter 3 of Mansfield and Bruckheimer: *Background to Set and Group Theory* (Chatto and Windus). The particular discussion for Boolean algebras can be found in the third reference above (but beware, for the notation is different in places).

It should be clearly borne in mind that the $\Leftrightarrow$ sign used in the Class Book means that the statements are logically equivalent and any statements whatever may be substituted for the 'variables'; the $\Leftrightarrow$ sign does not necessarily mean that they are the *same* statement. Thus $p \vee p' \Leftrightarrow t$ (on page 71) does not mean that 'what sir says is true or what sir says is not true' is the same as the fixed true statement (which may be 'apples are apples') but it is logically equivalent to it; i.e. it has the same truth values.

Exercise 5a Answers

1. (*a*) In the following table column 5 is the same as column 7 which verifies the required result.

a	b	a'	b'	$a \wedge b$	$a' \vee b'$	$(a' \vee b')'$
1	1	0	0	1	0	1
1	0	0	1	0	1	0
0	1	1	0	0	1	0
0	0	1	1	0	1	0

(*b*) In the following table column 6 is the same as column 8 which verifies the required result.

a	b	c	$a \wedge b$	$a \wedge c$	$(a \wedge b) \vee (a \wedge c)$	$b \vee c$	$a \wedge (b \vee c)$
1	1	1	1	1	1	1	1
1	1	0	1	0	1	1	1
1	0	1	0	1	1	1	1
0	1	1	0	0	0	1	0
1	0	0	0	0	0	0	0
0	1	0	0	0	0	1	0
0	0	1	0	0	0	1	0
0	0	0	0	0	0	0	0

2. (*a*) I cannot do my homework.
   (*b*) I cannot do my homework and I don't care.
   (*c*) Either I cannot do my homework or I cannot understand it or both.
   (*d*) Same as (*c*). See 1(*a*).

3. The first sentence can be written $a' \wedge b' \wedge c'$ and the second $(a \vee b)' \wedge c'$.

   The dual of 1(a) is $a \vee b \Leftrightarrow (a' \wedge b')'$, whence

   $$(a \vee b)' \Leftrightarrow a' \wedge b'$$

   which proves that the two statements are logically equivalent.

4. (a) $\triangle$, the symmetric difference. The 'or both' which is excluded by the exclusive 'or' corresponds to the intersection of two sets which is excluded by $\triangle$.

   (b)

	b	
$\veebar$	0	1
a 0	0	1
1	1	0

   (c) The necessary tables are:

a	b	$a \veebar b$	$b \veebar a$
1	1	0	0
1	0	1	1
0	1	1	1
0	0	0	0

a	b	c	$a \veebar b$	$(a \veebar b) \veebar c$	$b \veebar c$	$a \veebar (b \veebar c)$
1	1	1	0	1	0	1
1	1	0	0	0	1	0
1	0	1	1	0	1	0
0	1	1	1	0	0	0
1	0	0	1	1	0	1
0	1	0	1	1	1	1
0	0	1	0	1	1	1
0	0	0	0	0	0	0

pp. 69–72 The analysis discussed in the examples uses the same sort of tables as before, but for a different purpose.

p. 70　The expression $(p \lor p') \land q$ corresponds to the statement 'It is raining or it is not raining, and I am tired', which obviously has the same truth value as q (see, also, Example 2). This is borne out again by the following table which shows the last column identical to the second.

p	q	p'	$p \lor p'$	$(p \lor p') \land q$
0	0	1	1	0
1	0	0	1	0
0	1	1	1	1
1	1	0	1	1

p. 70　In terms of the equivalence classes discussed in the note to Class Book, page 67, a tautology belongs to the class of statements which are always true.

pp. 71–72　'p implies q' occurs in the alternative forms 'p is sufficient for q', 'if p then q' and 'q is necessary for p'.

Another form for '$p \Leftrightarrow q$' is 'p is necessary and sufficient for q'. Note that $p \Rightarrow q$ and $p \Leftrightarrow q$ are themselves both statements and we may regard $\Rightarrow$ and $\Leftrightarrow$ as binary operations in the set of statements. Their tables are

$\Rightarrow$	0	1
0	1	1
1	0	1

$\Leftrightarrow$	0	1
0	1	0
1	0	1

This use of $\Leftrightarrow$ is not the same as that in, for instance, $a' \land b' \Leftrightarrow (a \lor b)'$: the difference is similar to the difference between $x^2 + 2x + 1 = 0$ and $x^2 + 2x + 1 = (x + 1)^2$, the latter being sometimes written $x^2 + 2x + 1 \equiv (x + 1)^2$. In the statement $p \Leftrightarrow q$, where p and q are simple statements, it is not true that we can substitute *any* two statements for p and q. 'Triangle A has three sides if and only if grass is green' is an example of a valid substitution, since both statements have the same truth value, but 'Triangle A is isosceles if and only if grass is green' is not valid for grass is green even if triangle A is not isosceles. On the other hand

$$a' \wedge b' \Leftrightarrow (a \vee b)'$$

is true whatever statements are substituted for a and b. Although $p \Leftrightarrow q$ is sometimes read as 'p is logically equivalent to q' it is better not to do this: it compares with reading $x^2 + 2x + 1 = 0$ as $x^2 + 2x + 1$ is equivalent to 0. But the other way round does no harm: to read $x^2 + 2x + 1 = (x + 1)^2$ as $x^2 + 2x + 1$ equals $(x + 1)^2$ is satisfactory: similarly to replace 'logical equivalence' by some weaker English phrase does no harm. (Rutherford, in the third reference above, uses 'material equivalence' for $p \Leftrightarrow q$.) The relation between the two uses of $\Leftrightarrow$ can be put as follows: if, for instance, p and q are not simple statements, but compound statements (that is statements made up of a finite number of simple true or false statements using the logical symbols like $\wedge$, $\vee$, $'$), and if $\Leftrightarrow$ denotes material equivalence, and if $p \Leftrightarrow q$ is a tautology, then $p \Leftrightarrow$ (is logically equivalent to) q. (For further information see Rutherford, who uses $\leftrightarrow$ for material equivalence and $\equiv$ (in the first place) and $\Leftrightarrow$ for logical equivalence.)

In fact, we can use $=$ throughout if we understand the proper uses made of this sign. We define the proper use of $=$ as an abbreviation for an equivalence relation in a set and this is always the use made of it when used properly. The particular equivalence relation involved must always be specified, either explicitly or from the context. Now both uses of $\Leftrightarrow$ are equivalence relations in the set of statements. A possible reason for not using $=$ for $\Leftrightarrow$ is that we should always make a point of drawing the reader's attention to the fact when there are one or more equivalence relations in the same context. Thus we would not write

$$x^2 + 2x + 1 = 0$$
$$= (x + 1)^2 = 0$$
$$= x = -1$$

for we have then used = in two different senses. If we wrote

$$x^2 + 2x + 1 = (x + 1)^2 = 0$$
$$= x = -1$$

we would be making three different uses of =.

Although it may not be necessary to go into all this in class a discussion of the difference between the two uses of ⇔ and the difference between ⇒ and ⇔ is very important. The many English expressions used for these symbols should also be mentioned. The use made of ⇔ and ⇒ in other parts of Book 4 is generally in the sense of logical equivalence and logical implication respectively.

Exercise 5b Answers

1. If a stands for 'I have money' then 'I haven't got no money' is $(a')' \Leftrightarrow a$ and is, therefore, true if a is true and false if a is false.

2. The table for (a) is

p	q	q'	$q' \vee p$	$p \vee (q' \vee p)$
1	1	0	1	1
1	0	1	1	1
0	1	0	0	0
0	0	1	1	1

Hence the sentence is *contingent*.

The table for (b) is

p	q	$p \wedge q$	p'	q'	$p' \wedge q'$	$(p \wedge q) \vee (p' \wedge q')$
1	1	1	0	0	0	1
1	0	0	0	1	0	0
0	1	0	1	0	0	0
0	0	0	1	1	1	1

Hence the sentence is *contingent*.

The table for (*c*) is

p	*q*	*p*′	*q* ∨ *p*′	(*q* ∨ *p*′)′	*q* ∧ (*q* ∨ *p*′)′
1	1	0	1	0	0
1	0	0	0	1	0
0	1	1	1	0	0
0	0	1	1	0	0

Hence the sentence is *self-contradictory*.

The table for (*d*) is

p	*q*	*q* ∨ *p*′	*p* ∧ (*q* ∨ *p*′)	[*p* ∧ (*q* ∨ *p*′)]′	*q* ∨ [*p* ∧ (*q* ∨ *p*′)]′
1	1	1	1	0	1
1	0	0	0	1	1
0	1	1	0	1	1
0	0	1	0	1	1

Hence the sentence is a *tautology*. This last example corresponds, of course, to Example 2, page 70. Instead of using the table we could write

$$q \vee [p \wedge (q \vee p')]' \Leftrightarrow q \vee [p' \vee (q \vee p')']$$
$$\Leftrightarrow q \vee [p' \vee (q' \wedge p)]$$
$$\Leftrightarrow q \vee p' \vee (q' \wedge p)$$
$$\Leftrightarrow (q' \wedge p)' \vee (q' \wedge p)$$
$$\Leftrightarrow t.$$

In words the original expression is '(*p* implies *q* and *p* is true) implies *q* is true'.

3. If the 'or' is understood as the inclusive disjunction then the sentence in terms of *p*, *q* and *r* is [(*q*′ ∧ *p*′) ∧ (*r* ∨ *p*)]′. On the other hand, if the 'or' is understood as the exclusive disjunction then we have [(*q*′ ∧ *p*′) ∧ (*r* ⊻ *p*)]′. Since, as we have said, the expression 'or' without further comment is taken to be the inclusive disjunction, we shall analyse that case.

p	q	r	$r \vee p$	q'	p'	$q' \wedge p'$	$(q' \wedge p') \wedge (r \vee p)$	$[q' \wedge p' \wedge (r \vee p)]'$
0	0	0	0	1	1	1	0	1
1	0	0	1	1	0	0	0	1
0	1	0	0	0	1	0	0	1
1	1	0	1	0	0	0	0	1
0	0	1	1	1	1	1	1	0
1	0	1	1	1	0	0	0	1
0	1	1	1	0	1	0	0	1
1	1	1	1	0	0	0	0	1

The compound sentence is true unless 'I and you are young and he is old'. The simpler sentence could be 'It is not true that I and you are young and he is old'. (We assume that the negative of 'I am young' is 'I am old' – it should really be 'I am not young'. The whole problem of the negation of statements is difficult because of our abusive and imprecise use of the English language. For a discussion of this point see Allendoerfer and Oakley.)

4. (a) $(p' \wedge q') \vee (p \wedge q) \Leftrightarrow (p \Leftrightarrow q)$.

(b) $(p' \wedge q' \wedge r') \vee (p' \wedge q \wedge r') \vee (p \wedge q' \wedge r) \vee (p \wedge q \wedge r)$
$\Leftrightarrow p' \wedge [(q' \wedge r') \vee (q \wedge r')] \vee [p \wedge \{(q' \wedge r) \vee (q \wedge r)\}]$
$\Leftrightarrow p' \wedge [(q' \vee q) \wedge r'] \vee [p \wedge \{(q' \vee q) \wedge r\}]$
$\Leftrightarrow (p' \wedge r') \vee (p \wedge r)$ since $q' \vee q \Leftrightarrow t$
$\Leftrightarrow (p \Leftrightarrow r)$,

as a truth table readily shows.

* * * * *

p. 76 Switches can also be operated electrically. It is usual to denote all switches which behave like a given switch q, that is, are open when q is open and closed when q is closed, by the same letter q. So q really stands for a class of switches: compare the first use of $\Leftrightarrow$ for sentence logic. We have implicitly assumed this in the class text.

Because q stands for a class of switches we use $=$ to denote that two systems of switches behave in the same way, i.e. they belong to the same equivalence class of switches.

Exercise 5c Answers

1.

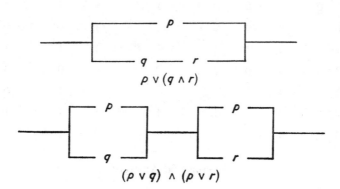

$$p \vee (q \wedge r)$$

$$(p \vee q) \wedge (p \vee r)$$

2.

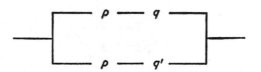

3. (a) Expression for switch is
$$(p \vee q) \wedge (p' \vee q) = q \vee (p \wedge p') = q \vee O = q.$$

(b) Expression for switch is
$$(p \vee q) \wedge (p' \vee q) \wedge (p \vee q') = [(p \wedge p') \vee q] \wedge (p \vee q')$$
$$= q \wedge (p \vee q')$$
$$= q \wedge p.$$

4. (a) $p \wedge (p' \vee q) = (p \wedge p') \vee (p \wedge q)$
$$= O \vee (p \wedge q)$$
$$= p \wedge q.$$

(b) The switches correspond to $(p \wedge q) \vee (p' \wedge r)$ and
$$(p \vee r) \wedge (p' \vee q).$$

Their equivalence is shown by the seventh and tenth columns in the following table.

p	q	r	$p \wedge q$	p'	$p' \wedge r$	$(p \wedge q) \vee (p' \wedge r)$	$p \vee r$	$p' \vee q$	$(p \vee r) \wedge (p' \vee q)$
1	1	1	1	0	0	1	1	1	1
1	1	0	1	0	0	1	1	1	1
1	0	1	0	0	0	0	1	0	0
0	1	1	0	1	1	1	1	1	1
1	0	0	0	0	0	0	1	0	0
0	1	0	0	1	0	0	0	1	0
0	0	1	0	1	1	1	1	1	1
0	0	0	0	1	0	0	0	1	0

Exercise 5d Answers

The table is

p	q	r
0	0	0
1	0	1
1	1	0
0	1	1

The corresponding expression is $(p \wedge q') \vee (p' \wedge q)$ with diagram

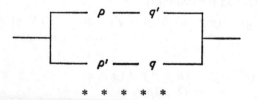

* * * * *

p. 80   There are, of course, many solutions to this problem.

Exercise 5e Answers

1. Many solutions. One is

p	q	r	t
1	1	1	1
1	1	0	0
1	0	0	1
1	0	1	0
0	0	1	1
0	1	1	0
0	1	0	1
0	0	0	0

The corresponding expression is

$(p \wedge q \wedge r) \vee (p \wedge q' \wedge r') \vee (p' \wedge q' \wedge r) \vee (p' \wedge q \wedge r')$

with diagram

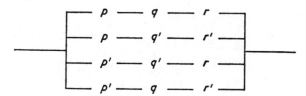

2. The live positions are given by

A	B	C	D
1	1	1	0
1	0	1	1
1	1	0	1

The corresponding expression is

$(A \wedge B \wedge C \wedge D') \vee (A \wedge B' \wedge C \wedge D) \vee (A \wedge B \wedge C' \wedge D)$

with diagram

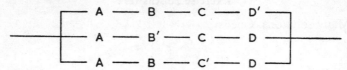

3. (a) $(q \wedge p') \vee (p \vee q') \Leftrightarrow t$.

   (b)

p	q	$q \wedge p'$
1	1	0
0	1	1
1	0	0
0	0	0

   (c) $p \veebar q \Leftrightarrow (p \wedge q') \vee (q \wedge p')$

   $p \barwedge q \Leftrightarrow (p \vee q') \wedge (q \vee p')$. This corresponds to $\circledast$ in set algebra.

MISCELLANEOUS EXERCISES II Answers

1. (a) {3, 5}

   (b) $\pi(A) = 30$, $\pi(B) = 105$, $\pi(A \cap B) = 15$. $\pi(A \cap B)$ is the highest factor common to $\pi(A)$ and $\pi(B)$.

   (c) $\pi(C) = 1540$, $A \cap C = \{5\}$, $\pi(A \cap C) = 5$, which is not the highest common factor of $\pi(A)$ and $\pi(C)$.

   (d) A sufficient condition is that the elements are prime numbers. A less severe condition is that no element of either set should be an integral multiple (by a factor other than 1) of any other element.

2. Denote the stopping of the machine by 0 and a thrown switch by 0. Then, assuming that the 'or' in the question is used in the inclusive sense and that 'two' means 'two or more', the machine will run if and only if one of the following patterns applies.

a	b	c	d	machine
1	0	1	1	1
1	1	0	1	1
1	1	1	0	1
1	1	1	1	1

   The appropriate Boolean function for the switches is

   $(a \wedge b' \wedge c \wedge d) \vee (a \wedge b \wedge c' \wedge d)$
   $$\vee (a \wedge b \wedge c \wedge d') \vee (a \wedge b \wedge c \wedge d).$$

   A simplified circuit might look like the following.

   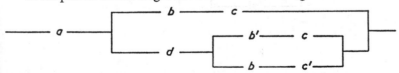

3. (a) $p \wedge q'$ represents 'Sir is always right and the answer in the book is incorrect'.

   $p \vee q'$ represents 'Sir is always right or the answer in the book is incorrect or both'.

(b) (i) tautology, (ii) contingent.

4. (a)

X	Y	X ∪ Y	X ∩ (X ∪ Y)	X ∩ Y	X ∪ (X ∩ Y)
1	1	1	1	1	1
1	0	1	1	0	1
0	1	1	0	0	0
0	0	0	0	0	0

The result is verified because the first, fourth and sixth columns are identical.

(b) A proof of 'A ∩ X = A ∩ Y and A ∪ X = A ∪ Y together imply X = Y'.

$$X = X \cap (X \cup A) = X \cap (A \cup Y) = (X \cap A) \cup (X \cap Y)$$
$$= (A \cap Y) \cup (X \cap Y) = (A \cup X) \cap Y = (A \cup Y) \cap Y$$
$$= Y.$$

Suppose that A′ and A′₁ are two complements of A, then we have A ∩ A′ = A ∩ A′₁ = ∅ and A ∪ A′ = A ∪ A′₁ = $\mathscr{E}$, hence A = A′₁.

5. (a) The Boolean function corresponding to the circuit is

$$\{p \land (q \lor r) \land s'\} \lor \{r' \land q' \land (p \lor s)\}$$

the dual is $\{p \lor (q \land r) \lor s'\} \land \{r' \lor q' \land (p \lor s)\}$.

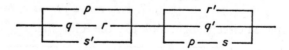

(b)

p	q	r	$(q \lor r)'$	$p \land q'$	$(p \land r)'$	$(p \land q') \land (p \land r)'$	$p \land (q \lor r)'$
1	1	1	0	0	0	0	0
1	1	0	0	0	1	0	0
1	0	1	0	1	0	0	0
0	1	1	0	0	1	0	0
1	0	0	1	1	1	1	1
0	1	0	0	0	1	0	0
0	0	1	0	0	1	0	0
0	0	0	1	0	1	0	0

The result is verified because the seventh and eighth columns are identical.

6. (a) The result is verified because the fifth and eighth columns below are identical.

A	B	C	$B \cup C$	$A \triangle (B \cup C)$	$A \cup B \cup C$	$A \cap (B \cup C)$	$(A \cup B \cup C) \sim [A \cap (B \cup C)]$
1	1	1	1	0	1	1	0
1	0	1	1	0	1	1	0
1	1	0	1	0	1	1	0
0	1	1	1	1	1	0	1
1	0	0	0	1	1	0	1
0	1	0	1	1	1	0	1
0	0	1	1	1	1	0	1
0	0	0	0	0	0	0	0

(b) $A \triangle (B \cup C) = (A' \cap B \cap C) \cup (A \cap B' \cap C')$
$\cup (A' \cap B \cap C') \cup (A' \cap B' \cap C).$

7. (a)

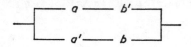

(b)

(c)

8. Note that in the left-hand part of the diagram below we have shown a set A as 'contained' in a set B if operations exist in A and B so that A is isomorphic to a subset of B.

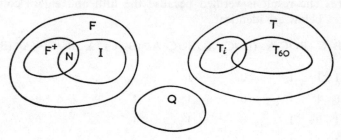

9. (a)

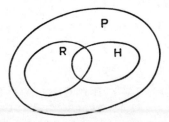

(b) $H \cap R = S$; $K \cap P = H$; $H \cap P' = \emptyset$.

CHAPTER SIX

The Solution of Quadratic Equations

GENERAL NOTES

The majority of topics in this chapter and the next are traditional and 'General Remarks' seem unnecessary.

NOTES ON TEXT OF CLASS BOOK
AND ANSWERS TO EXERCISES

p. 85   It is important to emphasise the basic properties (or absence of properties) of the operations we use, and we take every opportunity to do so.

Exercise 6a Answers

(*a*) $2 + 3 \times 4$ usually means $2 + (3 \times 4)$ and not $(2 + 3) \times 4$.
(*b*) Usually means $(3 \times 4) + 2$.
(*c*) Usually means $(3 - 2) + 4$.
(*d*) $3 + 2 - 4$ is unambiguous: $(3 + 2) - 4 = 3 + (2 - 4)$.

* * * * *

p. 86   We have already mentioned the irrationality of $\sqrt{2}$ in Teachers' Book 3, page 28. If the suggested work was not done there, here would be another good point to discuss irrational numbers in general and $\sqrt{2}$ in particular.

p. 86   The combination of mappings here is, of course, quite different from the combination discussed in Chapter 1. There, if r and s are as in the Class Book, the combination of r and s would be

$$r \circ s : x \longrightarrow (2x - 1) - 5 = 2x - 6$$
or $$s \circ r : x \longrightarrow 2(x - 5) - 1 = 2x - 11$$

p. 87   Notice that for any real numbers a and b, we can have $ab = 1 \Leftarrow a = 1$ and $b = 1$, but not $ab = 1 \Rightarrow a$ or $b = 1$.

Exercise 6b Answers

The purpose of this exercise is to make the very important point that $ab = 0 \Leftrightarrow a = 0$ or $b = 0$ is not a property possessed by all mathematical entities with which the pupil is familiar. It is of great value to point out from time to time as appropriate the differences in other systems: it helps to highlight the major points and to give them the same weight as the technical details.

(a) There are many possible divisors of zero: examples are

$$\begin{pmatrix} 1 & 0 \\ 0 & 0 \end{pmatrix}, \begin{pmatrix} 0 & 0 \\ 0 & 1 \end{pmatrix}; \begin{pmatrix} 1 & 0 \\ 0 & 0 \end{pmatrix}, \begin{pmatrix} 0 & 0 \\ 1 & 0 \end{pmatrix}; \begin{pmatrix} 1 & 1 \\ 1 & 1 \end{pmatrix}, \begin{pmatrix} 1 & 1 \\ -1 & -1 \end{pmatrix}.$$

(b) Again there are many: for example $\begin{pmatrix} 0 & 0 \\ 1 & 0 \end{pmatrix}, \begin{pmatrix} 1 & 1 \\ -1 & -1 \end{pmatrix}$. In general any matrix $\begin{pmatrix} a & b \\ c & d \end{pmatrix}$ which satisfies the four equations

$$a^2 + bc = 0 \qquad (a + d)b = 0$$
$$d^2 + bc = 0 \qquad (a + d)c = 0,$$

whence we get, for instance,

$$\begin{pmatrix} 0 & 1 \\ 0 & 0 \end{pmatrix}, \begin{pmatrix} -1 & 1 \\ -1 & 1 \end{pmatrix}, \begin{pmatrix} 1 & -1 \\ 1 & -1 \end{pmatrix}, \begin{pmatrix} -1 & -1 \\ 1 & 1 \end{pmatrix},$$

(c) A further example is congruence to a composite modulus.

* * * * *

p. 88 An alternative approach to the next few pages would be to discuss the expansion of $(X + A)(X + B)$ and by substituting successively $A = -B$, $A = B$ and $A = B = -C$, obtain the three fundamental results.

p. 89 Notice that we ignore the fact that we should write the third line of the working $(X^2 - XA) + (AX - A^2)$ and then justify the removal of the brackets. But, in fact, the removal of the brackets cannot be justified except by the abuse of notation remarked on in Exercise 6a, so we have omitted this step. Also, it should again be emphasised that the step $-XA + AX = 0$ is possible here but, perhaps, not elsewhere: e.g. if X and A are the matrices $\begin{pmatrix} 1 & 0 \\ 0 & 2 \end{pmatrix}$ and $\begin{pmatrix} 1 & -1 \\ 0 & 2 \end{pmatrix}$.

p. 89 Many teachers may like to use the geometric interpretation
of equation (1) given by the following diagram.

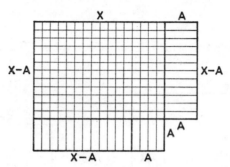

$(X - A)(X + A)$ is shown shaded horizontally, X^2 is shown
shaded vertically. The difference between them is the difference between the vertically shaded rectangle at the bottom
and the horizontally shaded rectangle at the right, which is
the small vertically shaded square.

pp. 89-91 Each of the six examples is designed to demonstrate a
particular point.

p. 90 The implication sign as used in Example 3 must be read
'which implies'. This is, of course, an abuse.

p. 90 It must be emphasised that $6(x^2 - 4) = 0 \Leftrightarrow x^2 - 4 = 0$ is
valid only because $6 \neq 0$. If it were $x(x^2 - 4) = 0$ then we
could not say that this implies $x^2 - 4 = 0$. The implication is
$x = 0$ or $x^2 - 4 = 0$. See Example 6.

Exercise 6c Answers

1. (a) 19   (b) 5200   (c) 52   (d) 352   (e) 480 (f) 198
   (g) 673·75.

2. (a) $x = \pm 3$ (b) $x = \pm 3$ (c) $x = \pm \frac{1}{5}$ (d) $x = \pm 2$
   (e) $x = \pm 10$ (f) $x = \pm \frac{7}{3}$ (g) $x = \pm \frac{1}{3}$ (h) $x = \pm \frac{1}{5}$

   (i) $x = \pm 2\sqrt{2}$ (j) $x = \pm \dfrac{1}{\sqrt{2}} = \pm \dfrac{\sqrt{2}}{2}$ (k) $x = \pm \dfrac{\sqrt{11}}{2}$

   (l) $x = \pm \dfrac{\sqrt{5}}{3}$.

3. (*a*) $x = 0$ or $x = 3$ (*b*) $x = 0$ or 3 (*c*) $x = 0$ or 4
   (*d*) $x = \pm\,3$ (*e*) $x = \pm\,2$ (*f*) $x = 0$ or $-\sqrt{5}$.

*   *   *   *   *

p. 92   The diagrams which illustrate equations (2) and (3) are given below

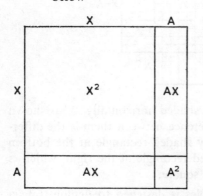 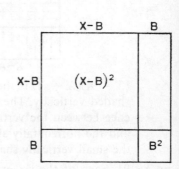

In the second diagram the whole large square represents X^2. In order to get $(X - B)^2$ we have to take away the overlapping rectangular pieces, each of area XB, except that we have taken the overlap away twice: hence add B^2 back in again to obtain the final result.

Exercise 6d Answers

1. $(X + A)^2 = (X + A)(X + A)$
$$= X(X + A) + A(X + A) \text{ distributivity of } \times \text{ over } +.$$
$$= X^2 + XA + AX + A^2 \text{ ditto, and associativity of } +.$$
$$= X^2 + 2AX + A^2 \text{ commutativity of } \times.$$

2. (*a*) $x^2 + 6x + 9$
  (*b*) $x^2 - x + \frac{1}{4}$
  (*c*) $a^2x^2 + 2ax + 1$
  (*d*) $\dfrac{x^2}{4} - x + 1$.

3. (a) $(x + 2)^2$ (b) $(x - 2)^2$ (c) $(x - \frac{3}{4})^2$
   (d) $(x - \frac{1}{7})^2$ (e) $(x + \frac{1}{14})^2$ (f) $(2x + 1)^2$.

4. (a) 16 (b) 16 (c) $\frac{9}{4}$ (d) 4 (e) 4 (f) 1 (g) $\frac{4}{13}$ (h) $\frac{4}{13}$.

* * * * *

p. 93   It might be worth mentioning to the class that having completed the square in a quadratic expression, we can deduce
the maximum or minimum value of the corresponding mapping. Thus if the mapping becomes

$$x \longrightarrow (x + a)^2 \pm b^2$$

then the least value taken by the image corresponds to
$x = -a$, since the square of a real number is always non-
negative. (This idea is also helpful in sketching the graph of
such a mapping. See Chapter 9, note to Class Book, page 145,
where we discuss the sketch in connection with inequalities.)
In other words the least numerical value of the image is b^2.
The onto range of the mapping is $\{x : x \geqslant + b^2\}$ or

$$\{x : x \geqslant - b^2\}.$$

If the mapping became

$$x \longrightarrow - (x + a)^2 \pm b^2$$

the image would have a maximum numerically equal to b^2.

p. 95   We feel we ought to apologise for perpetuating the sort of
nonsense statement $i^2 = -1$. If you are interested in a possible way of introducing complex numbers properly see the
article on this subject by M. Bruckheimer and N. Gowar in
the May 1965 issue of *Mathematics Teaching*.

p. 95   We have deliberately separated the problem of completing
the square and factorising a quadratic expression from the
problem of solving a quadratic equation. Too many pupils
when faced with a quadratic expression solve the corresponding quadratic equation whether this is appropriate to the
problem or not. This seems to be because they remember the
formula and nothing else.

p. 97   We make no attempt to explain the meaning of 'coefficient'
since this is best done verbally.

Exercise 6e Answers

1. -5 or -1 2. ± 4 3. 2 or 3   4. 0 or 6
5. 3 or 7   6. -2 or 6   7. $-3 \pm \sqrt{5}$ 8. $\pm \sqrt{7}$

9. 0 or 7   10. 3 or 4   11. $\dfrac{7 \pm \sqrt{5}}{2}$ 12. 5 or $\frac{3}{2}$

13. $\dfrac{4}{3}$ or $\dfrac{-3}{2}$ 14. $\dfrac{1 \pm \sqrt{17}}{4}$ 15. 5 or 3   16. $2 \pm \frac{1}{2}\sqrt{6}$.

Exercise 6f Answers

1. (a) $4 \pm \sqrt{2}$ (b) $6 \pm \sqrt{30}$ (c) $\frac{1}{2}$ or $\frac{9}{2}$

(d) $\dfrac{3 \pm i}{2}$ (e) $\dfrac{-1 \pm \sqrt{5}}{2}$ (f) $\frac{3}{2}$ or $-\frac{2}{3}$.

2. (a) 1 or -7 (b) 1·4 or $-\cdot 18$ (c) 1 or ·25
(d) ·5 or 1·2   (e) ± 1.

CHAPTER SEVEN

Factorisation and Graphical Methods

GENERAL NOTES

The subject matter of this chapter is again well known and notes are hardly necessary. We have tried to emphasise the basic principles underlying the techniques: it is impossible to repeat them often enough.

NOTES ON TEXT OF CLASS BOOK AND ANSWERS TO EXERCISES

p. 104 In Example 2 we come across the question of what do we mean by the factors of a mapping. The mapping $x \longrightarrow x^2 + 2$ has no 'real factors' but it has 'complex factors'. We touch upon this in the note at the beginning of Exercise 7a.

It should also be mentioned that 'factorise' means write as a product, as it does in the expression 'factorise 225'. Thus on page 105 when we have

$$x^2 - y^2 + x + y = x(x + 1) + y(1 - y)$$

we have not answered the problem, much the same as if we wrote

$$225 = (5^2 \times 2^3) + 5^2.$$

p. 104 In Example 2 the factorised form of $x \longrightarrow x^2 + 2$ is

$$x \longrightarrow (x + \sqrt{2}i)(x - \sqrt{2}i).$$

Exercise 7a Answers

1. $x \longrightarrow x(x + 4)$.
2. $y \longrightarrow 3(y^2 + 3)$ or $y \longrightarrow 3(y + \sqrt{3}i)(y - \sqrt{3}i)$.
3. $z \longrightarrow z(z^2 + z + 3)$ or $z \longrightarrow z\left(z + \dfrac{1}{2} + \dfrac{\sqrt{11}}{2}i\right)\left(z + \dfrac{1}{2} - \dfrac{\sqrt{11}}{2}i\right)$.
4. $w \longrightarrow (w - 4)(w + 2)$.
5. $u \longrightarrow -16u$ or $u \longrightarrow -2^4u$.

Exercise 7b Answers

1. $(2x - 5y)(2x + 5y)$.
2. $(a - 3)(a + b)$.
3. $(z + 2y)(z - 2)$.
4. $2(z + 2)(z + 1)$.
5. $(x + y)(x + y + 1)$.

* * * * *

p. 106 In the analysis of the properties used in the working out of $(x + a)(x - a)$ we have said that we are using the associativity of addition at one stage, although subtraction seems to be involved. We could get over this by regarding '$-xa$' always as a short-hand notation for '$+ (-xa)$'. Subtraction, of course, is not associative. If the pupil can be made to see clearly the double use of the minus sign

  (i) as a symbol for an operation
  (ii) purely as a symbol to denote the additive inverse of the integer $+a$,

a very important point will have been made.

It is possible to make the situation very clear by considering an abstract group G with operation o, say, whose elements are $g, g', g'' \ldots$ Then if $\tilde{g}$ denotes the inverse element of g, we can define an inverse operation of o, denoted by $\tilde{\delta}$, by

$$g' \tilde{\delta} g = g' \text{ o } \tilde{g}.$$

(This operation can be shown to be non-associative in general.) If we interpret G as the set of real numbers, o as addition, then $\tilde{\delta}$ is defined by

$$g' \tilde{\delta} g = g' + (-g).$$

Thus $\tilde{\delta}$ would seem to be what we call subtraction, but if we denote $\tilde{\delta}$ by the symbol '$-$' then this '$-$' has a different significance from that in $(-g)$.

p. 106 In Example 7 we use the subtraction of matrices which has not been explicitly defined. It can either be defined independently in an obvious way, or as the inverse operation of matrix addition, as described in the previous note.

Exercise 7c Answers

1. Since matrix multiplication is not commutative we need to state both equations; the first states that matrix multiplication is distributive from the left and the second states that it is distributive from the right.

2. $\begin{pmatrix} 6 & 2 \\ -2 & 2 \end{pmatrix}$

3. (a) $2(A + 2I)(A + I)$ or $2(A + I)(A + 2I)$

   (b) $A(B + C + I)$

   (c) $(A + B)(A + B + I)$. It should be pointed out that the matrix expression $A^2 + B^2 + 2AB \neq (A + B)^2$ in general. The class might be asked to try to factorise

   $$A^2 + B^2 + 2AB + A + B.$$

   Even grouping the terms to obtain

   $$A(A + B + I) + (A + B + I)B$$

   does not help.

* * * * *

p. 108 The integral factors of $x^2 + 8x + 12$ are $(x + 6)$ and $(x + 2)$.

Exercise 7d Answers

1. $(x + 4)(x + 2)$.
2. $(x - 4)(x - 2)$.
3. $(x - 4)(x - 3)$.
4. $(x - 19)(x + 2)$.
5. $(x - 5)(x + 2)$.

Exercise 7e Answers

1. (a) $(x - 4)(x + 3)$

   (b) $(5x - 1)(x + 1)$

   (c) $(2x - 1)(x + 2)$

   (d) $(3x - 2)(2x + 3)$.

2. (a) $(3x - 2)(2x + 5)$

   (b) $(4x + 5)(3x - 4)$

   (c) $(9x + 4)(4x - 3)$.

Exercise 7f Answers

1. $x - 1$.
2. $(x - 1)(x + 1)(x + 2)$.
3. $x + 4$.
4. $x + 6$.
5. $x - 1$.

* * * * *

p. 112 If we set out the second division sum in the following form the connection should be obvious.

$$
\begin{array}{r}
9(10)^3 + 8(10)^2 + 9(10) \\
(10)^2 - 2 \overline{\smash{\big)}\ 9(10)^5 + 6(10)^4 + 9(10)^3 + 9(10)^2 + 0(10) + 6} \\
9(10)^5 - 2 \times 9(10)^3 \\
= 9(10)^5 - (10)^4 - 8(10)^3 \\
\hline
7(10)^4 + 17(10)^3 + 9(10)^2 + 0(10) + 6 \\
= 8(10)^4 + 7(10)^3 + 9(10)^2 + 0(10) + 6 \\
8(10)^4 - 16(10)^2 \\
= 8(10)^4 - (10)^3 - 6(10)^2 \\
\hline
8(10)^3 + 15(10)^2 + 0(10) + 6 \\
= 9(10)^3 + 5(10)^2 + 0(10) + 6
\end{array}
$$

etc. The slight complication arises because in this type of setting out x has been given the definite value 10 and we have tried to obtain the form of the Class Book explicitly. We could also write

$$
\begin{array}{r}
9(10)^3 + 6(10)^2 + 27(10) \\
(10)^2 - 2 \overline{\smash{\big)}\ 9(10)^5 + 6(10)^4 + 9(10)^3 + 9(10)^2 + 0(10) + 6} \\
9(10)^5 - 18(10)^3 \\
\hline
6(10)^4 + 27(10)^3 + 9(10)^2 + 0(10) + 6 \\
6(10)^4 - 12(10)^2 \\
\hline
27(10)^3 + 21(10)^2 + 0(10) + 6
\end{array}
$$

etc., which, of course, gives the same answer and is more straightforward. It shows the same principle. If it is suggested that the divisor be written $9(10) + 8$, the best thing is to try it.

Exercise 7g Answers

1. (1) $(x - 1)(x^2 - 5x - 2)$
   (2) $(x - 1)(x + 1)(x + 2)$

(3) $(x + 4)(x^2 - x + 2)$

(4) $(x + 6)(x^2 + x - 1)$.

2. The other factor is $x^2 + ax + a^2$.

    (a) 2368

    (b) $- 8·911$

    (c) $(x + a)(x^2 - ax + a^2)$.

Exercise 7h Answers

1. The roots of the equation lie in the intervals $- 3 < x < - 2$, $- 1 < x < 0$ and $2 < x < 3$. The largest root is approximately $2·6(7) \simeq 2·7$.

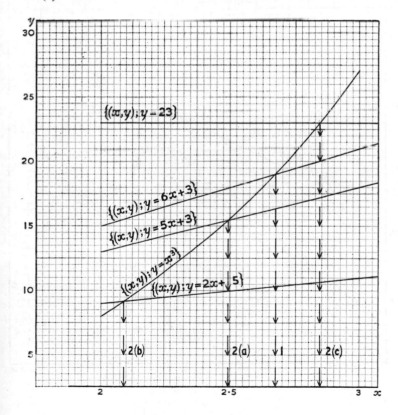

2. (a) 2·5
   (b) 2·1
   (c) 2·8.

3. The root of this equation can be located between 2 and 3. It is approximately equal to 2·6(6).

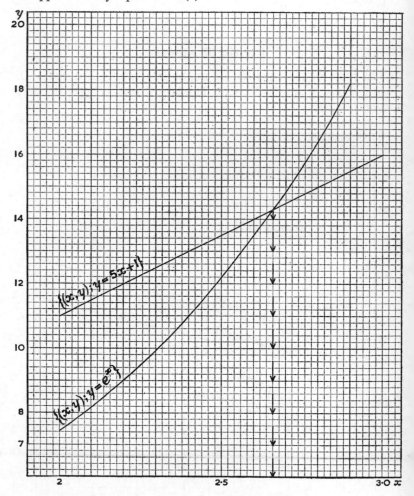

We have not discussed 'significant figures' anywhere in the Class Books. It requires definition at some time. When any number has been written in decimal form then the number of significant figures is the number of digits which are assumed to be correct reading from left to right (and ignoring any zeros on the left). Thus ·0136 and 136 (assuming all digits correct) both possess three significant figures.

When rounding off a number to so many significant figures the following conventions obtain. (For simplicity we shall take a particular case.) If we want to round off 14·93756 to six significant figures we retain the six digits 14·9375 and because ·00006 is more than half a digit in the sixth place, i.e. ·00006 > $\frac{1}{2}$ (·0001), we add one to the sixth digit obtaining 14·9376. If we round off the same number to three significant figures we get 14·9, since ·03756 < $\frac{1}{2}$(·1).

There are two possible ambiguities.

(i) 14·945 to four significant figures, since ·005 = $\frac{1}{2}$(·01). This is defined to be 14·94. In general the rounding off is done to the nearest even digit. Thus 17·955 to four significant figures becomes 17·96.

(ii) 1400. Are we indicating two or four significant figures? It is usual therefore to write 14×10^2 in the case of two and $14·00 \times 10^2$ in the case of four significant figures.

* * * * *

p. 115 We discuss inequalities in a little more detail in Chapter 9.

MISCELLANEOUS EXERCISES III Answers

1. (a) 7   (b) $2y^2 - xy = y(2y - x)$ (c) $(y - z)(y - 5)$.

2.

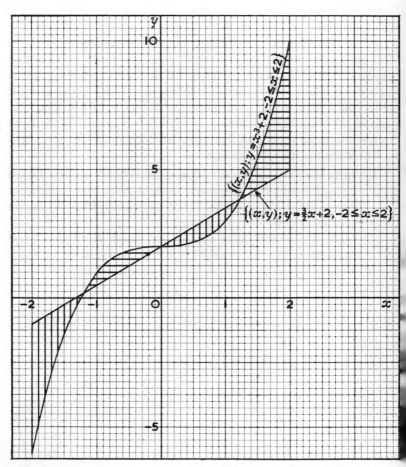

3. $(x + 6)(x + 24) - x(x + 18) = 360$, 648 sq in, 1008 sq in.
4. (a) true   (b) true   (c) true   (d) false.
5. (i) after $3\frac{3}{4}$ sec   (ii) 2·9 sec approx.
6. (a) $\pm 2a$ (b) -6, $x - 1$, $x - 3$.

7. (a) $(x^2 - 2x + 2)(2x + 1)(x - 3)$ (b) £17.
8. (i) £14,500   (ii) $6, -\frac{3}{5}$.
9. $9, -14, -21, -26, -24, -19, -11$
     (a) -26 (b) -1.22 to 2.05.
10. (i) $a = 2, b = 5, c = 4$ (ii) $p = 4\frac{1}{8}, q = 3\frac{7}{8}$.
11. $x^2 - 2x + 1, \frac{1}{2}$ or $1\frac{1}{2}$.
12. (i) $x(3x + 1)(x - 2)$ (ii) $(x - a + 4)(x - a - 4)$
     (iii) $(x - 3y)(x - 2)$.
13. $1.83, 1, 1.6$ (i) 0.5 (ii) $1.44, 5.56$.
14. (i) $3.2, 5$ (ii) $2.44, 6.56$ (iii) 2.44 to 6.56.
15. (i) $(x + 4)(x - 2)$ (ii) $(2x - 3)(2x + 3)$;
     (iii) $(x - 2)(x^2 + 2x + 4)$.

CHAPTER EIGHT

Flow Diagrams, Computer Programming

GENERAL NOTES

From a purely educational point of view pupils of all abilities can gain a lot from a brief and very general study of computer programming: the necessity for breaking complex procedures down into simple steps helps to reveal and clarify a pupil's weaknesses.

Some G.C.E. O level syllabuses require a somewhat more detailed and technical knowledge of certain computer features than is given in the Class Book: these details are found interesting by many pupils and they would have vocational value for a minority, but their value in terms of mathematical education is more doubtful. Hence short notes on these topics appear in the Teachers' Book only, and references to more adequate sources appear in 'Extra Reading for the Teacher' below.

The chapter begins with some work on flow diagrams. Plainly it would be better to wait until the need for a flow diagram arises in practice but this is never likely to occur in the classroom: in the absence of a computer the problems which can be undertaken are so straightforward that the programme (many people use the American spelling of this word, i.e. program: we shall not do so) itself can usually be written down at once, without a preliminary flow diagram. Hence our approach is somewhat artificial: we talk about flow diagrams as if they were essential preliminaries to the writing of programmes, while the actual programmes written are so simple as not to need a preliminary diagram at all. It would be as well to explain this to the class in advance, and to defend the procedure on the grounds that, for a real programme of any consequence on a real computer, the flow diagram is in fact an essential preliminary.

We ignore the multitude of special conventions which exist in this subject: they all have technical justification but little educational value in a description of this sort.

EXTRA READING FOR THE TEACHER

Ideally suited for those syllabuses which require some knowledge of input and output methods, memory stores, etc., are the two booklets *Computers 1* and *Computers 2* by Lovis, in the Contemporary School Mathematics Series published by Arnold.

Somewhat more technical is Burnett-Hill, Dresel and Samet: *Computer Programming and Autocodes* (E.U.P., 1964).

NOTES ON TEXT OF CLASS BOOK AND ANSWERS TO EXERCISES

p. 118 It should be pointed out that in most cases several quite different flow diagrams are all equally correct: in practice, of course, one uses the most economical programme. (Although economy of computer time and effort is by no means synonymous with economy of the programmer's time and effort.)

Exercise 8a Answers

1. We have not yet specified our 'computer language', so we have not restricted ourselves to simple two-possibilities tests. The diagram which follows uses a three-possibilities test and would therefore not be acceptable for the machine we will later describe.

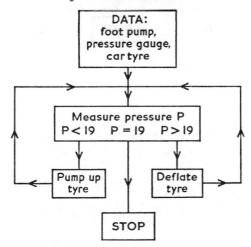

2. Neither in this diagram, nor in the programmes which follow, do we attempt to deal with the problem of the degree of accuracy required, although there would be no difficulty in incorporating the appropriate instruction in the diagram.

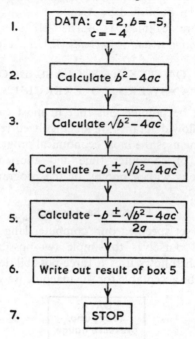

1.   DATA: $a = 2, b = -5, c = -4$

2.   Calculate $b^2 - 4ac$

3.   Calculate $\sqrt{b^2 - 4ac}$

4.   Calculate $-b \pm \sqrt{b^2 - 4ac}$

5.   Calculate $\dfrac{-b \pm \sqrt{b^2 - 4ac}}{2a}$

6.   Write out result of box 5

7.   STOP

3.

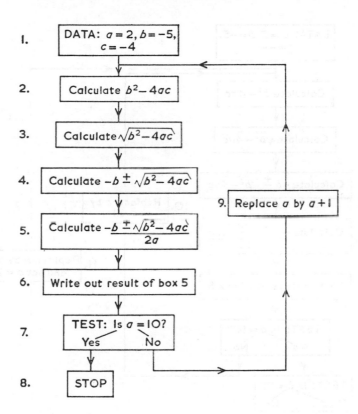

1. DATA: $a = 2, b = -5,$ $c = -4$

2. Calculate $b^2 - 4ac$

3. Calculate $\sqrt{b^2 - 4ac}$

4. Calculate $-b \pm \sqrt{b^2 - 4ac}$

5. Calculate $\dfrac{-b \pm \sqrt{b^2 - 4ac}}{2a}$

6. Write out result of box 5

7. TEST: Is $a = 10$? Yes   No

8. STOP

9. Replace a by $a + 1$

4.

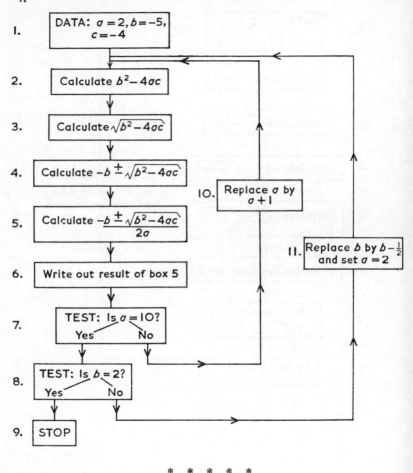

1. DATA: $a = 2, b = -5,$ $c = -4$

2. Calculate $b^2 - 4ac$

3. Calculate $\sqrt{b^2 - 4ac}$

4. Calculate $-b \pm \sqrt{b^2 - 4ac}$

5. Calculate $\dfrac{-b \pm \sqrt{b^2 - 4ac}}{2a}$

6. Write out result of box 5

7. TEST: Is $a = 10$? Yes No

8. TEST: Is $b = 2$? Yes No

9. STOP

10. Replace a by $a + 1$

11. Replace b by $b - \frac{1}{2}$ and set $a = 2$

* * * * *

p. 123 It will usually be found that pupils are interested in the methods by which information or programmes are put into and obtained from a computer. The methods in common use all depend on the binary scale, the information being presented in the form of a multitude of *bits*, each bit being a binary digit of the 0-1 or Yes-No type. For example, the input (and output) may be cards or paper tape in each position of which a hole is either punched or not punched. Alternatively, and less commonly, metal wire or tape may be used, each section being magnetised or not magnetised. In use, cards are relatively slow and clumsy, but are often used in accounting systems because they are robust and the information on them can be easily read by eye. Paper tape is faster but more fragile, and the information on it is usually extracted (or imprinted) by means of a special machine resembling a typewriter. Magnetic tape is the fastest: the information on it is not visible at all and a special machine must be used.

It may well be possible to obtain some punched cards or tape: pupils will be interested in deciphering the information on them.

The methods by which information is stored in a computer are also of interest. Of course, cards and tape (paper or magnetic) can be used as a 'memory' but there is usually a need for very fast access to each piece of information and this cannot be achieved by sorting cards or running through whole spools of tape. In fact, most computers have a 'slow' store and a 'fast' store. Fast stores usually depend upon some sort of matrix or mesh, the information being stored at the intersections of the mesh in the form, for instance, of magnetised or non-magnetised ferrite rods (or a circulating or non-circulating current in minute rings of super-conducting material): the information is extracted by passing a current along the wires which meet at the particular mesh intersection required.

For further information about input and output methods and stores, see the booklets by Lovis mentioned in 'Extra Reading for the Teacher'.

pp. 123–8 It must be clearly understood that the primitive language described here bears very little resemblance to that in use on any actual computer. The basic principles are similar, but a multitude of small but essential details have been suppressed for the sake of clarity.

Exercise 8b Answers

1. The series of instructions means that x_7 will contain the number
$$x_2 x_1^2 + x_1 x_3 + x_4.$$
x_6 will contain $x_1 x_3$ and x_3 will contain x_3.

2. 16.

3. $x_1 \times x_1 \rightarrow x_4$
$x_1 \times x_2 \rightarrow x_5$
$x_4 + x_5 \rightarrow x_4$
$x_4 + x_3 \rightarrow x_4$
$x_1 - x_2 \rightarrow x_5$
$x_4 \div x_5 \rightarrow x_4$
$\sqrt{x_4} \quad \rightarrow x_4$

Note that it is common practice to economise in the use of storage positions: although this very simple programme requires three positions to store the data and seven operations have to be performed, there is no need to use up ten storage positions: x_4, for example, is used five times.

* * * * *

pp. 125–9 Many improvements and modifications could be made to this programme. Some of these should be found by the pupils and discussed in class. For example, there is no need for the 2 and the -1 to be inserted in the data: the $2a$ can be achieved by $(a + a)$ and the -1 can be replaced by subtraction. It is well worth while for pupils to rewrite the programme using as data a, b, c and 4 only: the number of resulting changes is quite substantial.

Exercise 8c Answers

Before one can rely on a programme, one should test all possibilities that may arise. At the very least one must find data which make the programme follow each of its possible paths. In this case we have three possibilities which are tested by this exercise.

1.

INSTRUCTIONS

	DATA	1	2	3	4	5	⋯	16	⋯	22	23
x_1	2										
x_2	−3										
x_3	4	8	32								
x_4	4			9	−23						
x_5	2										
x_6	−1										
x_7											
x_8											

Column 5: TEST: −23 ≤ 0 JUMP to 16
Column 16: TEST: −23 < 0 JUMP to 22
Column 22: PRINT COMPLEX ROOTS — Column 23: OFF

2.

INSTRUCTIONS

	DATA	1	2	3	4	5	⋯	16	17	18	19	20	21	⋯
x_1	4													
x_2	−12								12	1·5				
x_3	9	36	144											
x_4	4			144	0						8			
x_5	2													
x_6	−1													
x_7														
x_8														

Column 5: TEST: 0 ≤ 0 JUMP to 16
Column 17: TEST: 0 = 0
Column 20: PRINT 1·5 EQUAL ROOTS — Column 21: OFF

3.

INSTRUCTIONS

	DATA	1	2	3	4	5	6	7	8	9	10	11	12	13	14	15
x_1	1											2				
x_2	5							−5								
x_3	1	1	4													
x_4	4			25	21		4·583			−4·583						
x_5	2															
x_6	−1															
x_7									−·417				−·2035			
x_8											−9·883			−4·7915		

Column 5: TEST: 21 > 0
Column 14: PRINT −·2035 and −4·7915 — Column 15: OFF

* * * * *

p. 131 The systematic procedure of the flow diagram, applied to the
particular case $x^2 - 3x - 10 = 0$, shows very clearly the
great difference between the mechanical approach and the

usual human method of intelligent guesswork. Pupils should be encouraged to work through the diagram in detail: they will find that they 'go round the loop' four times before obtaining $x_6 = -5$: this gives a 'yes' to the test and prints the roots as 5 and -2.

p. 131 A possible programme for the flow diagram on p. 130 is given below. As is quite common, this looped programme includes the modification in the main programme (instruction 1). It could equally well be put immediately after instruction 12, in the loop itself, prior to jumping to instruction 2. If this programme is given to the class they should work some 'dummy runs' on it.

READ DATA $a \rightarrow x_1$
$b \rightarrow x_2$
$-1 \rightarrow x_3$
$1 \rightarrow x_4$.
$0 \rightarrow x_5$.

FOLLOW INSTRUCTIONS

1   $x_4 + x_5 \rightarrow x_5$
2   $x_1 - x_5 \rightarrow x_6$
3   $x_5 \times x_6 \rightarrow x_7$
4   TEST If $x_7 \neq x_2$ JUMP to 9
5   $x_3 \times x_5 \rightarrow x_8$ (Note that instructions 5 and 6 are
6   $x_3 \times x_6 \rightarrow x_9$ necessary because we cannot tell our
7   PRINT x_8 machine to print $-x_5$.)
       x_9
8   OFF
9   $x_3 \times x_5 \rightarrow x_6$
10   $x_1 - x_6 \rightarrow x_7$
11   $x_6 \times x_7 \rightarrow x_8$
12   TEST If $x_8 \neq x_2$ JUMP to 1
13   $x_3 \times x_6 \rightarrow x_9$
14   $x_3 \times x_7 \rightarrow x_{10}$
15   PRINT x_9
       x_{10}
16   OFF.

p. 132 A possible programme for the flow diagram on p. 131 is given below. Modifications and improvements are possible: they should be discussed with the class.

READ DATA $1 \rightarrow x_1$
$0 \rightarrow x_3$
$1 \rightarrow x_4$
$a \rightarrow x_5$
$b \rightarrow x_6$

FOLLOW INSTRUCTIONS

1   $x_6 : x_1 \rightarrow x_2$
2   TEST If x_2 integral JUMP to 5
3   $x_1 + x_4 \rightarrow x_1$
4   JUMP to 1
5   TEST If $x_1 + x_2 \neq x_5$ JUMP to 10
6   $x_3 - x_1 \rightarrow x_1$
7   $x_3 - x_2 \rightarrow x_2$
8   PRINT x_1
           x_2
9   OFF
10 $x_1 + x_2 \rightarrow x_7$
11 $x_3 - x_7 \rightarrow x_7$
12 TEST If $x_7 \neq x_5$ JUMP to 3
13 PRINT x_1
           x_2
14 OFF.

Exercise 8d Answers

1.

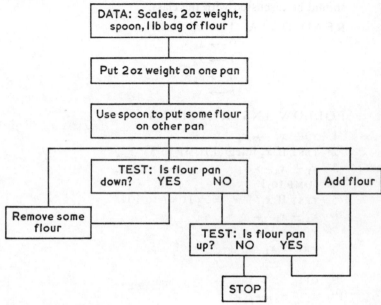

2. READ DATA $a \rightarrow x_1$
$$b \rightarrow x_2$$
$$c \rightarrow x_3$$
$$d \rightarrow x_4$$

FOLLOW INSTRUCTIONS

1 $x_1 \times x_4 \rightarrow x_1$
2 $x_2 \times x_3 \rightarrow x_2$
3 $x_1 - x_2 \rightarrow x_1$
4 PRINT x_1
5 OFF.

3. READ DATA $a \rightarrow x_1$
$$b \rightarrow x_2$$
$$c \rightarrow x_3$$
$$d \rightarrow x_4$$
$$0 \rightarrow x_5$$

FOLLOW INSTRUCTIONS

1   $x_1 \times x_4 \rightarrow x_6$
2   $x_2 \times x_3 \rightarrow x_7$
3   $x_6 - x_7 \rightarrow x_6$
4   TEST If $x_6 \neq 0$ JUMP to 7
5   PRINT NO INVERSE
6   OFF
7   $x_1 \div x_6 \rightarrow x_1$
8   $x_2 \div x_6 \rightarrow x_2$
9   $x_3 \div x_6 \rightarrow x_3$
10 $x_4 \div x_6 \rightarrow x_4$
11 $x_5 - x_2 \rightarrow x_2$
12 $x_5 - x_3 \rightarrow x_3$
13 PRINT x_4
$$x_2$$
$$x_3$$
$$x_1$$
14 OFF.

4. The following possible programme is exceedingly primitive! For example, in practice, instructions 31 to 39 would be replaced by one run through numbers 1 to 9 again. This would mean introducing the concept of a 'counter'.

READ DATA $a \rightarrow x_1$
$$b \rightarrow x_2$$
etc.
$$j \rightarrow x_{10}$$
$$10 \rightarrow x_{11}$$

FOLLOW INSTRUCTIONS

1   $x_1 + x_2 \rightarrow x_{12}$
2   $x_{12} + x_3 \rightarrow x_{12}$
3   $x_{12} + x_4 \rightarrow x_{12}$
. . . .
. . . .

9    $x_{12} + x_{10} \longrightarrow x_{12}$

10    $x_{12} \div x_{11} \longrightarrow x_{12}$

11    $x_1 - x_{12} \longrightarrow x_1$

12    $x_2 - x_{12} \longrightarrow x_2$

    . . . .

    . . . .

20    $x_{10} - x_{12} \longrightarrow x_{10}$

21    $x_1 \times x_1 \longrightarrow x_1$

22    $x_2 \times x_2 \longrightarrow x_2$

    . . . .

    . . . .

30    $x_{10} \times x_{10} \longrightarrow x_{10}$

31    $x_1 + x_2 \longrightarrow x_{12}$

32    $x_{12} + x_3 \longrightarrow x_{12}$

    . . . .

    . . . .

39    $x_{12} + x_{10} \longrightarrow x_{12}$

40    $x_{12} \div x_{11} \longrightarrow x_{12}$

41    $\sqrt{x_{12}} \longrightarrow x_{12}$

42   PRINT x_{12}

43   OFF.

CHAPTER NINE

Ordering: Percentiles: Inequalities

GENERAL NOTES

IN this chapter we have connected various statistical ideas with the concept of ordering in a set of objects. Previously in this series of texts, the only type of relation specifically investigated was the equivalence relation. One should not give the impression that this is the only type of relation which is of importance and so we begin with a closer study of relations in general. This topic can be taken to extremes (we hope we have not done this) but on the other hand a discussion, based on a series of examples, can lead to a better understanding of the differences between the various relations which occur. In particular, the realisation that $<$ has different properties from $=$, and that, in consequence, it will behave differently, should help the student to approach the manipulation of inequalities without misconceptions. Most students fight shy of inequalities either because they have never been introduced to them at all, or because the basic distinction between this relation and the relation of equality has never been made clear. Inequalities are not harder equalities, but something different.

When discussing ordering as such, it can be pointed out that one set can often be ordered in a number of different ways, depending on the purpose. The pupils should be able to find examples about them of this sort of situation. It will probably be much more interesting for them to discuss sets and relations which they have discovered, than to work too many examples which are presented to them.

Following on from the discussion of ordering relations, we consider the general problem of defining certain statistical quantities in a totally ordered set. The notes on the text of the Class Book highlight some of the difficulties. Once again, it would probably be more interesting to analyse the situations which the pupils create.

We then return to the problem of 'solving an inequality' in the set of real numbers. It is useful to compare the process with that of 'solving an equation' in order to point out the differences, but it should be made clear from the start that we are looking for the differences; we do not expect the two processes to be the same, and we must be careful not to create the wrong impression. We compare in order to contrast, not to be surprised by the differences, but deliberately to discuss them. The real similarity lies in the description of the problem. The solution of an equation or an 'inequation' is the problem of finding the set of elements x whose image under a given mapping f falls within a given set A. If we write the equation and 'inequation' in the standard forms

$$f(x) = 0 \quad \text{and} \quad f(x) > 0$$

then, for the equation, A is the set whose only element is 0 and, for the 'inequation', A is the set of all positive numbers.

Finally in this chapter we return to the statistical concept of sampling and the significance for the whole population of such quantities as the median and mean calculated from a simple. This connects directly with the previous statistical discussion and there is no need to interrupt with the discussion of inequalities.

EXTRA READING FOR THE TEACHER

Any standard text on statistics may be helpful. The sections on inequalities in Allendoerfer and Oakley: *Principles of Mathematics* (McGraw-Hill) are well worth reading.

NOTES ON TEXT OF CLASS BOOK
AND ANSWERS TO EXERCISES

p. 134 It is important that both the set and the relation should be accurately stated before any discussion. For instance 'a precedes b' can be a total or a partial ordering, depending on the set in which it is defined.

p. 135 The terms used for the various types of ordering are not the only ones in common use. If any other books are consulted then the definitions of the terms used should be carefully scrutinised.

p. 135 It is probably easier to understand the classification of relations if it is partially tabulated as follows:

	Equivalence	Ordering	
		Special	Strict
reflexive	✓	✓	×
symmetric	✓	×	×
transitive	✓	✓	✓

p. 135 Example 1. When there is a book lying on the top of the others the relation 'to the left of' becomes partial.

p. 135 Example 2 introduces the notations ⊆, ⊂.

Exercise 9a Answers

1. (*a*) Yes (*b*) No (*c*) Yes (*d*) Yes (*e*) No (*f*) Special ordering, partial.

2. (*a*) No (*b*) No (*c*) No (*d*) Yes (*e*) Yes (*f*) Strict ordering, total.

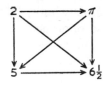

3. (*a*) No (*b*) Yes (*c*) No (*d*) No (*e*) No (*f*) It is neither an ordering nor an equivalence relation.

4. Special ordering, total.

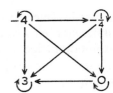

5. Equivalence relation.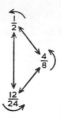

6. Equivalence relation. A circle centre the origin describes each equivalence class.

7. Strict ordering, partial.

8. Strict ordering, total.

9.

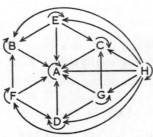

10. 42 has the three prime factors 2, 3 and 7. If instead of any number we write the set of the prime factors (if the same prime occurs several times, each appearance should be distinguished, say by a suffix), then 'x divides exactly into y' is equivalent to 'the set of prime factors of x is contained in the set of prime factors of y'. Note that 1 is not a prime number and corresponds to the null set.

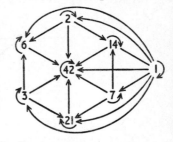

*   *   *   *   *

p. 138 Another case in which seemingly identical elements are considered different occurs when defining the H.C.F. and L.C.M. using set notation. See Teachers' Book 3, page 17.

p. 139 In a case such as the set of books mentioned in the class text, the median itself, even if it existed, would probably be meaningless. After all the whole point in determining the median (or mean or mode) of a set of statistical quantities is that we should have one fact (or facts) which is in some sense representative of the whole. If all we have done is to put books on a shelf as they came to hand and we find that there is an odd number of books then mathematically the median is defined as the central book, but the fact that the central book is *A History of the Great War* can tell us nothing about the set as a whole. The mathematical existence of a quantity does not imply that this quantity is necessarily significant or meaningful. This is true not only in statistics, but almost everywhere.

It is precisely for this reason that we sometimes take the mean as a more useful representative, sometimes the mode, sometimes the median, sometimes something else: sometimes we can find nothing sufficiently representative. For instance, if in one department of a big firm the manager has a salary of £2000, whereas the other six employees, who are clerks and typists, have salaries between £800 and £1100, then the mean is a poor representative of the 'average' salary. One might describe this by saying that the median was a more stable 'average' under a small number of extreme fluctuations. In each statistical enquiry one must be very careful not to give more weight to the mathematically defined facts than the context permits. That the median is in fact a statistically useful quantity depends, basically, upon the number of elements being large, and the central elements being almost indistinguishable from one another in respect of the property considered in the ordering relation, so that one may take either of the central elements without too much inaccuracy. Similar considerations apply to quantities similar to the median, for example, the quartiles.

p. 140   The semi-interquartile range is defined only if the ordering relation is such that the difference between two elements is defined and can meaningfully be divided by two: if, for instance, in a row of books, the upper quartile is *Gone With The Wind* and the lower quartile is *The Bible*, the semi-inter-

tile range is undefined. Of course, as we said about the median, even when all the quantities are defined, any or all may be contextually meaningless.

Exercise 9b Answers

1. D, E, A, C, B.

   (a) A

   (b) The median number of elements would be the same in this case, since ordering the sets by $<$ according to the number of their elements would give the same order.

   (c) The sets are now not totally ordered by $\subset$, but there would be a median number of elements since $<$ is still total ordering.

2. (a) White   (b) Black   (c) Yellow.

Note that we can use the relation in (a) to order the *sets* of men as well, i.e. set A precedes set B if the men in A are taller than in B. We would then have a median class, which in this case is white. But it is not necessary that the median man and median class coincide: for instance if the population were

     black (3)   red (1)   white (1)   yellow (6)   green (5),

then the median man would be yellow and the median class white.

3. A possible answer is

$$x_1 = 3,\ x_2 = 2,\ x_3 = 1,\ x_4 = 1,\ x_5 = 6.$$

Mean $= 5$ (to the nearest whole number of peas)
median $= 6$, mode $= 7$.

4.

Column A	Column B
100	485
90	480
80	470
70	445
60	385
50	295
40	175
30	75
20	25
10	5

   (a) Median $\simeq 45 \cdot 7$, (b) lower quartile $\simeq 34 \cdot 6$, upper quartile $\simeq 57 \cdot 6$,
(c) 40th percentile $\simeq 41 \cdot 6$.

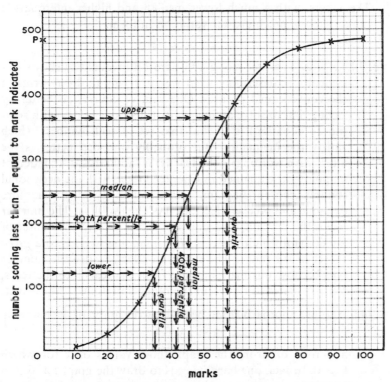

5. Presumably one reason is that one could get many 'freak' situations: for example a batsman who batted only once and then for some reason did not bat again for some weeks; if he scored 121 in that one innings, he would always be top of the averages—but this would have little significance. Another possibility could be a bowler who always bats at number eleven, who might have a series of scores like

0 n.o., 12, 2 n.o., 17 n.o., 10 n.o., 0 n.o., 10 n.o.,

This would give him an average of 51, higher than many a regular batsman.

The average (i.e. mean) shows little difference between the three batsmen, but the median together with the semi-interquartile range shows that 75% of the innings of batsman B were over 37.

The others, with a much lower median and higher interquartile range, show a much greater variation in form.

* * * * *

pp. 145 et seq. The first paragraph here on inequalities shows our difficulty in describing what we are trying to do in terms of the conventional phrases. One can, of course, do better by saying that to solve an inequality (in strict analogy with solving an equation) is to find that set of real numbers which satisfy the inequality. But probably one step better is the alternative wording: if the teacher is familiar with the idea of mappings as explained in Chapter 1 then, with the occasional suitably chosen diagram, this terminology allows a more dynamic and precise description of the problem. The number line is the domain, and our problem is to find the subset of the domain which under a *given* mapping maps into a *given* subset of the range. The range, in effect, is also the number line, because our mappings are from the reals into the reals, but it is better to represent the range and domain as distinct.

p. 145 Another approach could be to draw the graph of the mapping

$$x \longrightarrow 23x - 3(2x^2 + 7) = P$$

and read off from the graph those values of x for which $P > 0$. In fact, one hardly needs to draw the graph: a sketch is sufficient, and to find the exact values of a and b we can solve a quadratic equation. Thus the above mapping is roughly represented by the following sketch

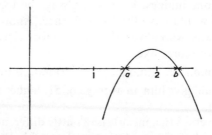

on which the points a and b are shown.

The sketch of a quadratic expression is either like the one shown i.e., with 'nose' upward, or upside down.

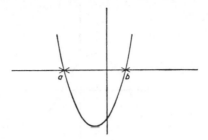

In this latter case the the solution for which the image is positive is $\{x; x < a\} \cup \{x; x > b\}$.

That there are only these two possibilities may not be immediately obvious. In the first place we might suppose that the 'nose' might also point sideways thus:

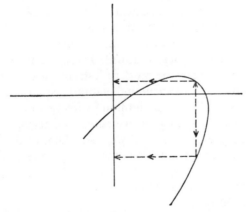

We can dispose of this possibility by noticing that our mapping is single-valued, whereas the sketch shows a double-valued mapping. (Of course, if the curve could have this position, it would still have a solution set of the form

$$\{x; a < x < b\},$$

but while we are at it we might as well get as much information about this mapping as we can.)

We might then suppose that the curve has two bends in it, for instance:

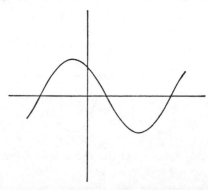

This would mean that we have three roots. In this sort of way any suggestions by the class can be dealt with and we shall always be brought back to our two first simple forms.

If this sort of discussion is followed, it should slowly dawn on the class that to find the solution set of a quadratic inequality, we need only know whether the curve is the 'right way up' or 'upside down'. There are many ways we can do this: perhaps the most pedestrian, at this level, would be to solve the corresponding quadratic equation, choose one value between the roots and find its image under the mapping. But out of any situation we should be trying to guide the class into discovering what we want them to discover. (It may be true that the best form of teaching is one in which the children discover things for themselves, but this does not preclude some guidance in order that they discover what might be useful.)

If the mapping is

$$x \longrightarrow Ax^2 + Bx + C$$

then if $A > 0$ the 'nose' of the sketch is downward; if $A < 0$ the 'nose' is upward. We can easily deduce this by discussing orders of magnitude and convincing ourselves that for large x, the term in x^2 dominates. Alternatively, we can lead on to a discussion of gradients.

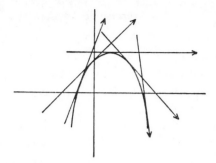

Passing along a curve such as that above the gradient decreases as x increases.

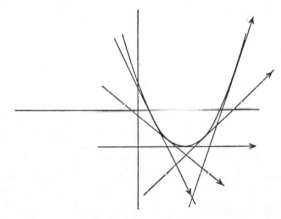

Passing along a curve such as that above the gradient increases as x increases. This in turn prepares the way for some work in calculus and harks back to the work on gradients in Chapter 2.

p. 147 Some teachers might like to link this discussion with the general discussion of ordered fields and integral domains; see, for instance, Birkhoff and Mac Lane: *A Survey of Modern Algebra* (Macmillan).

For further reading and extensions see Kazarinoff: *Analytic Inequalities* (Holt, Rinehart and Winston).

Exercise 9c Answers

1. In every case $a + c < b + c$.

2. In every case $a + c > b + c$ and it is a valid procedure to add the additive inverse of b to both sides of the inequality.

3. (a) Yes   (b) No   (c) Yes   (d) No   (e) Yes   (f) No
   (g) Yes   (h) No.
   $a < b \Leftrightarrow ca < cb$ if $c < 0$ and $a < b \Leftrightarrow ca > cb$ if $c < 0$.

4. $a > b \Leftrightarrow ac > bc$ if $c < 0$ and $a > b \Rightarrow ac < bc$ if $c < 0$.

5. $a < b \neq a^2 < b^2$. $a^2 < b^2 \Leftrightarrow a^2 - b^2 < 0 \Leftrightarrow (a - b)(a + b) < 0$ and if $a < b$, we have $a + b > 0$. Hence if $a + b = 0$ or $a + b < 0$ the result is not true. The implication holds only if $(a + b)$ is positive.

   It might be found advisable to try some numerical examples first as in Numbers 1 to 4: e.g.

   $$a = 1, b = 2; \quad a = -1, b = 1; \quad a = -2, b = -1.$$

6. $\{x; (3x - 4)(x - 2) < 0\} = \{x; \tfrac{4}{3} < x < 2\}$.

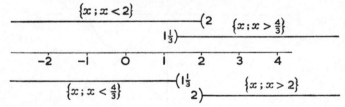

7. $\{x; -\tfrac{3}{2} < x \leqslant 5\}$.

8. $\{x; -5 < x < 2\} \cup \{x; x > 3\}$.
   It might be instructive to sketch the mapping in this question and discuss it.

Exercise 9d Answers

The means of the ten samples are $3\tfrac{2}{3}$, 4, $4\tfrac{1}{3}$, 6, $6\tfrac{1}{3}$, $6\tfrac{1}{3}$, $6\tfrac{2}{3}$, $6\tfrac{2}{3}$, 7, 9, with semi-interquartile range of $1\tfrac{1}{6}$.
The medians of the ten samples are 2, 2, 2, 8, 8, 8, 8, 9, 9, 9, with semi-interquartile range of $3\tfrac{1}{2}$.

* * * * *

p. 150 What 'chosen at random' means is intuitively obvious, and
       is usually put into some such words as 'A sample is random if
       every element of the whole population is equally likely to be
       chosen for the sample'.

       If we know *nothing* about a population and must make
       some estimate of it from a sample, then it is evident that the
       sample should be random. Otherwise, all sorts of bias can be
       introduced, as in the case of an advertiser who claims that
       97 women out of 100 use his detergent – he has probably
       chosen his 100 carefully, and not by any means at random.
       (Although he could easily find three more, he would be careful
       not to claim 100 out of 100 – this is probably significant of
       his intention to mislead, and of his opinion of the general
       public's idea of a sample!) Hence, in the absence of informa
       tion, a random sample is desirable; nevertheless it is not
       always easy to obtain in practice.

       In this connection one could discuss many claims made
       from popular surveys: e.g. opinion polls, B.B.C. broadcasting
       surveys and such statements as '4 out of every 5 who tried
       couldn't tell chalk from butter'.

p. 150 Many other devices can be used instead of a ten-sided spin-
       ner. It is impossible to make a spinner which is not biased
       (see Exercise 10c Number 2 for a possible way of dealing
       with this): in order to reduce the bias it must be made very
       carefully. In general other devices will probably be preferred.
       Tables of random numbers are available and can be pur-
       chased: for instance the Cambridge Statistical Tables contain
       such a table.

p. 150 One might perhaps discuss what should be done if, when
       choosing a random sample of ten numbers from 1 to 100,
       the same number appeared twice. (The answer will depend
       upon the purpose for which the sample is drawn up. In
       general, the second appearance of the same number would be
       rejected only if its inclusion was specifically likely to impair
       the efficiency of the sample. For example, if a party political
       canvasser, engaged in assessing the opinions of the electorate,

were to call upon ten householders at random in a road of one hundred houses, he would not call upon the same householder twice.)

Exercise 9e Answers

The device would be suitable for choosing the numbers from 5 to 95, but to obtain ten numbers in this range may require more than 20 spins: any number outside the range is just ignored. It could also be used for the range 0 to 100 in the same way, but the method might be very laborious.

To illustrate the possible trend in the discussion of any set of ten numbers obtained consider the following: suppose the sample obtained was:

06, 12, 24, 32, 34, 43, 54, 67, 78, 94.

Having obtained this sample, one might well be suspicious of it on the grounds that if each digit has an equal chance of being chosen, then, in ten two digit numbers, each digit should occur about twice: but in fact 4 occurs five times and 0, 1, 5, 8 and 9 occur once only. Does this mean that the sample is not, in fact, random? (That is, is it *biased*?) On the other hand, if one actually *chooses* the numbers, without using the spinner, so that each digit does occur exactly twice, then one could hardly claim that the sample was chosen at random! (See the next section, on layering.)

Dilemmas such as the above lead very rapidly into all sorts of logical and semantic difficulties and we shall not discuss them here: they are mentioned only to show that the idea of 'random choice', although vital to statistics, is by no means simple.

Exercise 9f Answers

It is, of course, impossible to give answers to Numbers 1 to 6, but the individual results must be interpreted. Even if some pupils obtain samples which do not confirm the theory, the whole set of results from the class should confirm it.

It would be an idea, time permitting, to get the class to undertake some project in which they design the method and then collect their own statistics: there are numerous possibilities within and around schools, and in general everyday experience.

7.

Samples	1, 2, 4	1, 2, 9	1, 4, 9	2, 4, 9
Mean	$2\frac{1}{3}$	4	$4\frac{2}{3}$	5
Mean deviation	$1\frac{1}{9}$	$3\frac{1}{3}$	$2\frac{8}{9}$	$2\frac{2}{3}$
Standard deviation	$\dfrac{\sqrt{14}}{3} \simeq 1\cdot2$	$\sqrt{\dfrac{38}{3}} \simeq 3\cdot6$	$\dfrac{7\sqrt{2}}{3} \simeq 3\cdot3$	$\sqrt{\dfrac{26}{3}} \simeq 2\cdot9$

	M	S
Mean	$2\frac{1}{2}$	$\simeq 2\cdot76$
Mean deviation	$\frac{25}{36} \simeq \cdot69$	$\simeq \cdot76$
Standard deviation	$\simeq \cdot84$	$\simeq \cdot9$

Here the mean deviations have a smaller scatter and hence would seem to be more efficient.

(For comment on text at end of Number 7 see below.)

8. S.D. of operator A $\simeq$ 1·4 thousands of an inch.
   S.D. of operator B $\simeq$ ·87 thousands of an inch.

* * * * *

p. 152 It might be mentioned that the square of the standard deviation is also used as a measure of scatter. It is known as the variance. The units in which the variance is expressed are often inconvenient.

p. 153 In fact the statement in the text is not explicit enough. Suppose that we have a population whose total size is n (which will in general be very large) and that we take *all* possible samples of size r and calculate the means of each of these samples. Let the set of all such means be M_r: we can find the mean of M_r and we will find that it is the same as the mean of the whole population. This result is easily proved, and like the next can be found in any elementary book on statistics.

Further we can find the scatter of the sample means about the mean, i.e. find the standard deviation of the set M_r. If σ_r is this standard deviation and σ is the standard deviation of the whole population then it can be proved that

$$\sigma_r{}^2 = \frac{n-r}{n-1} \frac{\sigma^2}{r}.$$

Hence we can use either standard deviation to calculate the other.

In practice with very large n, we can neither calculate σ nor σ_r, but the equation gives us a very useful piece of information. If n is large, then

$$\frac{n - r}{n - 1} \simeq 1.$$

With $n = 50{,}000{,}000$ and $r = 1000$, say (figures that might occur in a survey involving the population of Britain),

$$\frac{n - r}{n - 1} \simeq \cdot99998.$$

It follows that if we write $\sigma_r{}^2 \simeq \dfrac{\sigma^2}{r}$, then, when n is large, we have a very reasonable approximation.

Hence, for example

$$\sigma_{100} \simeq \frac{\sigma}{10}, \qquad \sigma_{900} \simeq \frac{\sigma}{30}.$$

This means that the error in taking a mean calculated from a sample of size 900 as an approximation to the population mean can be expected to be one-third of the error obtained by taking the mean of a sample of size 100. (Note, however, that we still have no idea of the actual error involved.)

Put in a slightly different way, the bigger the samples the more closely the means of the samples are scattered about the true mean.

SUGGESTIONS FOR FURTHER WORK

Clearly the amount of further work that is possible is endless. The discussion above, properly simplified, is an obvious extension: also some work could be started on correlation. Another obvious extension is to consider more complicated examples than in the text and to develop some of the short methods for calculating the mean and standard deviation.

In inequalities the treatment of 'modulus' questions such as $|x^2 - 3x + 4| > 0$ or $|x - 1| < |x + 2|$ can lead to interesting work and can be treated elegantly by graphical methods.

CHAPTER TEN

Probability

GENERAL NOTES

THE traditional approach to probability is usually successful in the very early stages but soon runs up against what, for most pupils, prove to be insuperable difficulties. Most pupils abandon hope altogether soon after what are often called 'compound probabilities' have been reached: at this stage, given a specific problem, the pupil finds that he can produce several different answers, only one of which can be right, but he has no means of telling which, if any, of his solutions is the correct one. His confidence is completely destroyed and he resolves to avoid probability questions if he can. This is demonstrated by an inspection of a sample of examination scripts where some choice of questions has been allowed: only the very best and the very worst candidates attempt the probability questions. The average candidate is firmly resolved to have nothing whatever to do with the topic.

The approach offered here is markedly different from the traditional one. It is axiomatic without being rigorous; once the axioms (here called 'statements') have been grasped there should be no difficulties later in the application of the system to particular problems.

The work on 'probability matrices' and Markov chains is well worth doing for interest's sake even if it is not required by the particular examination syllabus. It should be noted that the terminology in general use for this topic is rather complex and we have not attempted to use it: in particular, the terms 'probability matrix' and 'invariant matrix' are our own and have no validity elsewhere.

EXTRA READING FOR THE TEACHER

The following are recommended:

O.E.E.C. *Synopses for Modern Secondary School Mathematics*

Allendoerfer and Oakley: *Principles of Mathematics* (McGraw-Hill)

Kemeny, Snell and Thompson: *Introduction to Finite Mathematics* (Prentice-Hall).

NOTES ON TEXT OF CLASS BOOK
AND ANSWERS TO EXERCISES

p. 154 The direct product of two sets is often called their Cartesian product. The word 'product' is used because the number of elements in the direct product set is the product of the numbers of elements in the two sets. (This operation on sets can, in fact, be used to define multiplication of natural numbers.)

Exercise 10a Answers

1. $A \boxtimes B = \{(a_1,b_1), (a_1,b_2), (a_2,b_1), (a_2,b_2), (a_3,b_1), (a_3,b_2)\}$.

   $B \boxtimes A = \{(b_1,a_2), (b_1,a_2), (b_1,a_3), (b_2,a_1), (b_2,a_2), (b_2,a_3)\}$.

   The direct product operation is not commutative, for in the example given the elements of $A \boxtimes B$ are different from those of $B \boxtimes A$. It may be pointed out, however, that the numbers of elements in the two direct products are the same.

2. $A \boxtimes (B \boxtimes C) = \{(a_1,(b_1,c_1)), (a_1,(b_1,c_2)), (a_1,(b_2,c_1)), (a_1,(b_2,c_2)),$
   $(a_2,(b_1,c_1)), (a_2,(b_1,c_2)), (a_2,(b_2,c_1)), (a_2,(b_2,c_2)),$
   $(a_3,(b_1,c_1)), (a_3,(b_1,c_2)), (a_3,(b_2,c_1)), (a_3,(b_2,c_2))\}$.

   $(A \boxtimes B) \boxtimes C = \{((a_1,b_1),c_1)_2\ ((a_1,b_1),c_2), ((a_1,b_2),c_1), ((a_1,b_2),c_2),$
   $((a_2,b_1),c_1, ((a_2,b_1),c_2), ((a_2,b_2),c_1), ((a_2,b_2),c_2),$
   $((a_3,b_1),c_1), ((a_3,b_1),c_2), ((a_3,b_2),c_1), ((a_3,b_2),c_2)\}$.

   The direct product operation is not associative for, although the triples of elements are in the same order in the two cases, the brackets are arranged differently. For example, $(a_1,(b_1,c_1))$ is not the same as $((a_1,b_1),c_1)$.

3. Since $A \boxtimes (B \boxtimes C)$ is not the same as $(A \boxtimes B) \boxtimes C$ we can *define* $A \boxtimes B \boxtimes C$ (without brackets) to mean something different from either, and this is what is usually done.

   An example of such ordered triples corresponds to the case when each of the three sets is the set of all real numbers: the set of triples is then a three-dimensional co-ordinate system. (There are, of course, other interpretations and applications.)

4. A $\boxtimes$ B has nq elements, no matter whether or not the intersection of A and B is empty.

* * * * *

p. 155 It may be necessary to clarify what is meant by 'axiom'. It should certainly be pointed out that the axioms must not contradict one another (we check this by producing an actual example: if the axioms contradicted one another one could not construct an example). As remarked in the text, this is not a minimum set of axioms: S.3 and S.5 could, for example, be deduced from the others. It is for convenience alone that they are included as axioms, to avoid the necessity for proof.

p. 156 It might be interesting to *prove* that if E_1 with mapping p_1 and E_2 with mapping p_2 are two probability spaces (i.e. both satisfy S.1, S.2, S.3 and S.4) then, necessarily, $E_1 \boxtimes E_2$ with mapping p_3 given by $p_3(x,y) = p_1(x) \times p_2(y)$ is also a probability space. The only benefit to be obtained from this proof is that which comes from constructing it for oneself.

Exercise 10b Answers

(The 'proofs' given below have no more validity than the single statement 'both results are obvious from the diagrams'.)

(a) $(A \sim B) \cap (A \cap B) = \emptyset$ by the definition of $A \sim B$.

Hence, since $A \sim B$ and $A \cap B$ are both subsets of $A \cup B$, we may use S.3, taking $A \cup B$ as the sample space. Then

$$p[(A \sim B) \cup (A \cap B)] = p(A \sim B) + p(A \cap B).$$

But $(A \sim B) \cup (A \cap B) = A$, so

$$p(A) = p(A \sim B) + p(A \cap B)$$

i.e. $p(A) - p(A \cap B) = p(A \sim B)$.

(b) From (a) $p(A) = p(A \cap B) + p(A \sim B)$

and $p(B) = p(B \cap A) + p(B \sim A)$

Hence $p(A) + p(B) = 2p(A \cap B) + p(A \sim B) + p(B \sim A)$

(since $A \cap B = B \cap A$)

that is,

$$p(A) + p(B) - p(A \cap B) = p(A \cap B) + p(A \sim B) + p(B \sim A).$$

Now the sets named on the right-hand side of the '=' sign are all subsets of A ∪ B, their union is A ∪ B and they do not intersect each other: hence, by an obvious extension of S.3, the right-hand side is p(A ∪ B). This proves the result.

* * * * *

p. 158 When we say that the set of possible results (or 'outcomes') is known we do not imply that we know which particular result will occur: we merely know that the result must be some one of a known set.

The definition of an 'event' is important. Generally, events are sets whose elements are the results.

p. 158–9 These examples deserve careful study: it is this sort of approach that removes the doubt that most pupils begin to feel at about this stage.

We wish to emphasise the difference between theoretical and experimental probability. For example, even if the probabilities for the spinner on page 158 had been obtained experimentally, the probability for something like 'scored either 1 or 3' would be theoretical.

Exercise 10c Answers

1. (a) We require the subset corresponding to 'more than 2 or less than 3'. This is the union of the subsets 'more than 2' and 'less than 3'.

In E these are $\{3_A, 3_B\}$ and $\{0, 1, 2\}$. Hence, by S.3

probability $= (\frac{1}{5} + \frac{1}{5}) + (\frac{1}{5} + \frac{1}{5} + \frac{1}{5}) = 1.$

Alternatively, in F we have

$$\{3\} \quad \text{and} \quad \{0, 1, 2\}$$

whence probability $= (\frac{2}{5}) + (\frac{1}{5} + \frac{1}{5} + \frac{1}{5}) = 1.$

(It may be necessary to discuss the significance of the result.)

(b) 'Not scored a 3' corresponds, in both E and F, to $\{0, 1, 2\}$ and has probability $\frac{1}{5} + \frac{1}{5} + \frac{1}{5} = \frac{3}{5}$. The result can, of course, be obtained by observing that if A is some subset and $p(A) = a$, then necessarily $p(A') = 1 - a$, where A′ is the complement of A.

2. This question refers again to the ideas of experimental and theoretical probability first mentioned in Book 2 (page 68 et seq.). It is suggested, on intuitive grounds, that as the number of trials increases the experimental probability should approach the theoretical probability. A useful discussion is easily provoked by asking what we should do if this did not in fact happen.

* * * * *

p. 161 The pupils will no doubt discover for themselves the possibility of actually forming $A \cup B$ and then calculating $p(A \cup B)$, instead of using S.9. It is usually simpler.

Exercise 10d Answers

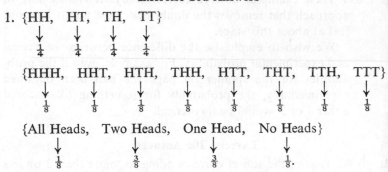

1. {HH, HT, TH, TT}
   $\downarrow$ $\downarrow$ $\downarrow$ $\downarrow$
   $\frac{1}{4}$ $\frac{1}{4}$ $\frac{1}{4}$ $\frac{1}{4}$

   {HHH, HHT, HTH, THH, HTT, THT, TTH, TTT}
   $\downarrow$ $\downarrow$ $\downarrow$ $\downarrow$ $\downarrow$ $\downarrow$ $\downarrow$ $\downarrow$
   $\frac{1}{8}$ $\frac{1}{8}$ $\frac{1}{8}$ $\frac{1}{8}$ $\frac{1}{8}$ $\frac{1}{8}$ $\frac{1}{8}$ $\frac{1}{8}$

   {All Heads, Two Heads, One Head, No Heads}
   $\downarrow$ $\downarrow$ $\downarrow$ $\downarrow$
   $\frac{1}{8}$ $\frac{3}{8}$ $\frac{3}{8}$ $\frac{1}{8}$.

2. The probability $\frac{1}{36}$ is allotted to each element.

   'Total score 2' corresponds to subset $\{(1,1)\}$ with probability $\frac{1}{36}$

   .. .. 3 .. .. .. $\{(1,2), (2,1)\}$ with probability $\frac{2}{36} = \frac{1}{18}$

   .. .. 4 .. .. .. $\{(1,3), (2,2), (3,1)\}$ with probability $\frac{3}{36} = \frac{1}{12}$

etc.

The full set of results is

Total score	2	3	4	5	6	7	8	9	10	11	12
Probability	$\frac{1}{36}$	$\frac{1}{18}$	$\frac{1}{12}$	$\frac{1}{9}$	$\frac{5}{36}$	$\frac{1}{6}$	$\frac{5}{36}$	$\frac{1}{9}$	$\frac{1}{12}$	$\frac{1}{18}$	$\frac{1}{36}$

Using the total score as the sample space, with the mapping just given, 'total is prime' corresponds to the subset $\{2, 3, 5, 7, 11\}$ which has probability $\frac{1}{36} + \frac{1}{18} + \frac{1}{9} + \frac{1}{6} + \frac{1}{18} = \frac{15}{36}$.

3. $\{2H, \quad 1H, \quad 0H\}$

$\qquad \downarrow \qquad \downarrow \qquad \downarrow$

$\quad \frac{1}{16} \qquad \frac{3}{8} \qquad \frac{9}{16}.$

For two throws, 'no head' is the most likely.

$\{4H, \quad 3H, \quad 2H, \quad 1H, \quad 0H\}$

$\quad \downarrow \qquad \downarrow \qquad \downarrow \qquad \downarrow \qquad \downarrow$

$\frac{1}{256} \quad \frac{12}{256} \quad \frac{54}{256} \quad \frac{108}{256} \quad \frac{81}{256}.$

For four throws, 'one head' is the most likely.

4. The total score probability space is: $\{2, \quad 3, \quad 4, \quad 5, \quad 6\}$

$\qquad\qquad\qquad\qquad\qquad\quad \downarrow \quad \downarrow \quad \downarrow \quad \downarrow \quad \downarrow$

$\qquad\qquad\qquad\qquad\qquad\quad \frac{1}{9} \quad \frac{2}{9} \quad \frac{3}{9} \quad \frac{2}{9} \quad \frac{1}{9}.$

The 'loses his sixpence' event is the set $\{4, 5\}$ which has probability $\frac{3}{9} + \frac{2}{9} = \frac{5}{9}$.

5. (a) In Number 4, $L = 6d$, $p_L = \frac{5}{9}$, $W = 6d$, $p_W = \frac{4}{9}$. Since $6 \times \frac{5}{9} \neq 6 \times \frac{4}{9}$, the game was not 'fair'.

   (b) We now have $L = 6d$, $p_L = \frac{8}{9}$, $p_W = \frac{1}{9}$.
   From $L \times p_L = W \times p_W$ we obtain $W = 48d$. A winning player should receive 48d plus his stake, that is, 4s 6d.

   (c) 'On the average', for every 9 trials, the machine will collect 4s 6d and return 4s. Thus the machine makes 6d profit for each 9 trials: hence 360 trials will probably cover the rent.

6. (a) $\frac{11}{125}$

   (b) 5s 8d

   (c) In the compound probability space the probability of three oranges is $\frac{2}{5} \times \frac{1}{5} \times \frac{2}{5} = \frac{4}{125}$, but the probability of three pears is $\frac{1}{5} \times \frac{3}{5} \times \frac{1}{5} = \frac{3}{125}$.

* * * * *

pp. 163–5 The point to be made here is that our choice of which compound probability space to use is governed entirely by the physical situation. It is easier to form what seem to be the two probability spaces than to form the single compound space using three 'simple' spaces although, as we point out subsequently (and as many pupils will realise), two events in each of the compound spaces (1) and (2) cannot occur.

Exercise 10e Answers

(a) $\frac{4}{663}$

(b) $\frac{4}{221}$

(c) $\frac{8}{663}$

(d) $\frac{11}{221}$

(e) $\frac{9}{221}$.

* * * * *

p. 167 It is valuable in many ways to illustrate the fact that, for most people, intuition is a very bad guide to probabilities.

The following problem is well known for its rather surprising result and can very profitably be discussed with suitable classes.

Example

There are 23 people in a room. Their birthdays are scattered at random. What is the probability that at least two of them were born on the same day of the same month (not necessarily in the same year)? (Assume that every year has 365 days.)

Take any one person and find his birthday.

Take a second person: what is the probability that his birthday is *not* the same as the first? He has 365 possible birthdays, of which 364 would be different from the first person's day. Hence the probability is $\frac{364}{365}$.

Take a third person. What is the probability that his birthday will not be the same as either of the first two? Again, he has 365 possible birthdays, of which 363 would be different from the other two (for two different days have been used already). Hence the probability is $\frac{363}{365}$.

Thus the probability that three persons' birthdays will all be different is $\dfrac{364}{365} \cdot \dfrac{363}{365}$.

Take a fourth person, and multiply $\dfrac{364}{365} \cdot \dfrac{363}{365}$ by $\dfrac{362}{365}$ to obtain $\dfrac{364.363.362}{365.365.365}$ as the probability that four persons' birthdays will all be different.

Similarly, the probability that five persons' birthdays will all be different is $\dfrac{364.363.362.361}{365.365.365.365}$.

Evidently, the probability that the birthdays of twenty-three persons will all be different is

$$\dfrac{364.363.362.361.360 \ldots \text{and so on, for 22 factors}}{365.365.365.365.365 \ldots \text{and so on, for 22 factors}}$$

$$= \dfrac{364.363.362. \ldots .344.343}{365^{22}}$$

$\simeq \cdot 49$ (using logarithms).

But this is the probability that all their birthdays are different. Our problem is to find the probability that at least two of their birthdays are the same. We have here an interpretation of S.6: the probability $\cdot 49$ and the probability we require are the probabilities of complementary events. Hence the probability that at least two birthdays are the same is approximately $1 - \cdot 49 = \cdot 51$. In other words, it is slightly more likely than not. Most people find this surprising: they feel that the probability should be much smaller.

Exercise 10f Answers

1. $\frac{45}{1176}$.

2. $\frac{13}{196}$.

3. $\frac{3}{51}$.

4. $\frac{1}{16}$.

5. In Numbers 1, 2 and 3 the direct product space is the product of two *different* spaces: in Number 4 the two sample spaces are both the same.

6. (a) $\frac{7}{16}$

   (b) $\frac{3}{8}$

   (c) Good $\frac{103}{256}$: Bad $\frac{153}{256}$.

Exercise 10g Answers

$$M = \begin{pmatrix} \frac{1}{4} & \frac{3}{4} \\ \frac{1}{2} & \frac{1}{2} \end{pmatrix} \qquad M^2 = \begin{pmatrix} \frac{7}{16} & \frac{9}{16} \\ \frac{3}{8} & \frac{5}{8} \end{pmatrix} \qquad M^3 = \begin{pmatrix} \frac{25}{64} & \frac{39}{64} \\ \frac{13}{32} & \frac{19}{32} \end{pmatrix}$$

$$M^4 = \begin{pmatrix} \frac{103}{256} & \frac{153}{256} \\ \frac{51}{128} & \frac{77}{128} \end{pmatrix}.$$

(a) $\frac{1}{2}$ (b) $\frac{19}{32}$ (c) $\frac{153}{256}$ (d) $\frac{39}{64}$ (using M^3).

* * * * *

p. 172   With suitable classes, it is easy to show that for any probability matrix $M = \begin{pmatrix} p & 1-p \\ q & 1-q \end{pmatrix}$ other than the unit matrix a unique probability matrix A exists to satisfy $AM = A$, and A is of the form $\begin{pmatrix} x & 1-x \\ x & 1-x \end{pmatrix}$ and hence has no inverse.

Notice, however, that we do not attempt to prove by such methods that if $AM = A$ then $M^n \rightarrow A$ although this is in fact true when all the elements of M are positive: we merely show that if M^n does tend to a limit then that limit must be A.

To prove that successive powers of a probability matrix (with all its elements positive) approach a limit would require more technique than we propose to develop here. (See 'Suggestions for further work'.) The result is almost intuitively obvious. An exception is readily seen in $\begin{pmatrix} 0 & 1 \\ 1 & 0 \end{pmatrix}$.

Exercise 10i Answers

1. (a) $\begin{pmatrix} \frac{5}{8} & \frac{3}{8} \\ \frac{3}{4} & \frac{1}{4} \end{pmatrix}$

   (b) $\begin{pmatrix} \frac{43}{64} & \frac{21}{64} \\ \frac{21}{32} & \frac{11}{32} \end{pmatrix}$

   (c) The proportion of rainy days to non-rainy days is 2 to 1.

2. There is nothing wrong with the argument provided that the inverse C exists. In fact if A is an invariant probability matrix for a probability matrix M then A has no inverse.

3.

$$\begin{array}{cc} & \text{E} \quad \text{W} \end{array}$$

The probability matrix is $\begin{array}{c} \text{E} \\ \text{W} \end{array}\begin{pmatrix} \frac{9}{10} & \frac{1}{10} \\ \frac{5}{8} & \frac{3}{8} \end{pmatrix}$.

The corresponding invariant matrix is $\begin{pmatrix} \frac{25}{29} & \frac{4}{29} \\ \frac{25}{29} & \frac{4}{29} \end{pmatrix}$.

The probability space in one year's time will be $\begin{array}{c} \{\text{East, West}\} \\ \downarrow \quad\quad \downarrow \\ \frac{25}{29} \quad\quad \frac{4}{29} \end{array}$.

86 per cent.

4.

$$\begin{array}{cc} & \text{R} \quad \text{L} \end{array}$$

In the form $\begin{array}{c} \text{R} \\ \text{L} \end{array}\begin{pmatrix} \frac{9}{10} & \frac{1}{10} \\ \frac{5}{8} & \frac{3}{8} \end{pmatrix}$ the matrix for gas A is identical with that of Number 3. Hence the invariant matrix for A is

$$\begin{pmatrix} \frac{25}{29} & \frac{4}{29} \\ \frac{25}{29} & \frac{4}{9} \end{pmatrix}$$

whence one would expect to find 86 per cent of gas A in the right-hand half.

The probability matrix for gas B is $\begin{array}{c} \text{R} \\ \text{L} \end{array}\begin{pmatrix} \frac{2}{3} & \frac{1}{3} \\ \frac{3}{4} & \frac{1}{4} \end{pmatrix}$ and the corresponding invariant matrix is

$$\begin{pmatrix} \frac{9}{13} & \frac{4}{13} \\ \frac{9}{13} & \frac{4}{13} \end{pmatrix}$$

so that one would expect to find $\frac{9}{13}$, i.e. 69 per cent of gas B in the right hand half.

If 100 molecules of gas A and 100 molecules of gas B were originally put in the container, one would expect the left-hand chamber to contain $100 - 86 = 14$ molecules of gas A and $100 - 69 = 31$ molecules of gas B.

(In other words, although the original mixture was of equal parts of A and B, the contents of the left-hand chamber would be in the ratio of 31 of B to 14 of A.)

5. {Alive, Dead}

$\downarrow$ $\downarrow$

·998001 ·001999.

1·999 times as likely (i.e. about twice as likely).

The invariant matrix is $\begin{pmatrix} 0 & 1 \\ 0 & 1 \end{pmatrix}$. It means that I shall eventually die and stay dead!

SUGGESTIONS FOR FURTHER WORK

With suitable pupils, eigenvalues and eigenvectors can be approached through their geometric interpretations: their applications to powers of probability matrices can then be dealt with. See, for example, Matthews: *Matrices* 2 (Arnold: Contemporary School Mathematics).

MISCELLANEOUS EXERCISES IV Answers

1. Central 90% of springs have heights between 1·022 and 1·11 inches approximately.
   Mean height is 1·065 inches and standard deviation is ·027 inches.
   Range of heights is from 1·01 to 1·12 inches.

2. (a) $5\frac{1}{2}$ (b) ·55   (c) 460   (d) a bar chart seems suitable.

3. $\frac{2}{3}$.

4. 45°.

5. (i) $\frac{7}{15}$.
   (ii) Probably the most important point to be brought out is that the advertisement does *not* claim that seven people out of *every* ten suffering from toothache are instantly cured.

6. (i) 73   (ii) 44·2%.

7. 6·17(5) in,   4·5 in,   6 in,   8·4(4) in,   4·1 in.

8. (i) $\frac{1}{120}$ (ii) $\frac{1}{6}$.

9. 22·15.

10. (a) $\frac{14}{33}$ (b) $\frac{16}{33}$ (c) $\frac{1}{11}$ (d) $\frac{19}{33}$.

CHAPTER ELEVEN

Isometries

GENERAL NOTES

IT should be clear that we cannot talk about proof in this chapter: our whole approach is intuitive. Therefore, the only sense in which we can be said to 'prove' a result is that in some sense we have made it more obvious. Our main aim is to learn a little about the group of isometries and its subgroups. The exercises are meant to lead up to the general results which follow and, on the whole, with guidance, the pupils should be able to discover the results for themselves. In the circumstances we have, probably, not always given the most 'elegant' demonstration: it is not always the best for teaching purposes.

A geometric transformation is a one-one mapping of the plane onto itself. It follows, therefore, that two transformations f and g are the same if for every point P of the plane

$$f(\text{P}) = g(\text{P}).$$

The commonest error is to deduce something about a transformation from one or two points and their images. It is important to make it clear from the outset that this can only lead to false conclusions. In fact, in the case of isometries, there is the fundamental result that an isometry is uniquely determined by three non-collinear points and their images: in other words, there is a unique isometry which maps a proper triangle into a distinct congruent triangle. (We discuss this result in Exercise 11f.) It follows that we can determine an isometry by considering what happens to three non-collinear points and our result will not be special. The fact that it is not always necessary to consider three points is fortuitous: we somehow feel (or even have reason to believe) that we have a general result, which, as we said, must be regarded as sufficient in an intuitive approach, unless someone produces a counter example.

Geometry, even the geometry of the group of isometries, is vast

136

and there is no end to the number of results one can obtain. We have, therefore, taken the view that because we can use it to illustrate algebraic structure and because it is amusing, one should play with geometry as long as it amuses, illustrates and time is available. There is enough material in the present chapter to satisfy most pupils: the majority will probably find it too much, and unless it is needed for examination purposes, as much can be left out as the teacher desires.

This chapter and the next are on the whole devoted to 'pure geometry', that is, we discuss the results by experiment in which a co-ordinate system, if used at all, is incidental. In Book 5 we shall spend a little space on discussing the corresponding co-ordinate geometry in which co-ordinates are used specifically, i.e. we consider 'algebraic geometry'.

EXTRA READING FOR THE TEACHER

H. S. M. Coxeter: *Introduction to Geometry* (Wiley).
I. M. Yaglom; *Geometric Transformations* (Random House).

NOTES ON TEXT OF CLASS BOOK
AND ANSWERS TO EXERCISES

p. 177   It is not usually a good idea to use actual physical mirrors to demonstrate reflections for the situation can become very confusing when two or more reflections are performed.

Exercise 11a Answers

1. (*a*) (i) $(1, -1)$ (ii) $(-1, -1)$
   (*b*) $(1, -1)$.

2. (i) Reflection in the line $y = -x$.
   (ii) Reflection in the line $y = x$.
      There is no single reflection which maps P onto P′ and Q onto Q′. (We never use 'reflection' in this chapter to mean 'reflection' in a point.)

3. (*a*) Clockwise.
   (*b*) Anticlockwise.

(c) No – a rotation does not change the sense of a triangle. (A rotation through 180° about the x-axis takes the figure out of the plane and is not admissible.)

(d) Yes – since the two triangles have the same sense it is possible. In fact, the rotation is about the origin through an angle of 180°. The general problem of the combination of two reflections is discussed in the subsequent text, but this result should be easy enough to discover. It might be instructive to map a few more points by the two reflections and show that the single rotation has the same effect.

The point brought out in the last question gives us the following partition of the group of all isometries:

(i) direct isometries, i.e. those isometries which do not change the sense of a triangle. This set is in fact a subgroup and consists of the translations and rotations.

(ii) indirect isometries, i.e. those isometries which do change the sense of a triangle. This set cannot be a subgroup since the combination of two 'sense-changing' isometries must preserve sense, and hence the set is not closed. We know that reflections belong to this set. Since the combination of a direct isometry and an indirect isometry must be indirect, the combination of a translation or a rotation with a reflection must also belong to this set. We shall discover in the course of the chapter that the only new single isometry so obtained is the so-called glide reflection (see Exercise 11f).

It is of interest to point out that the many-one mapping

$$\text{indirect isometry} \rightarrow -1$$
$$\text{direct isometry} \rightarrow +1$$

is a homomorphism (a homomorphism is also a structure-preserving mapping like an isomorphism, but unlike the isomorphism, which is one-one, a homomorphism is many-one) of the group of all isometries onto the multiplicative group with elements $+1$ and -1. This is illustrated by what we said above when we remarked that the combination of two indirect isometries $((-1) \times (-1))$ is a direct isometry $(+1)$; etc.

If we bear these results in mind we can make a preliminary

examination of any combination of isometries which we wish to discuss and decide to which subset it belongs.

$$* \quad * \quad * \quad * \quad *$$

p. 178 et seq. In general the figures given in the Class Book will mean very little—they just save a lot of words. Pupils should throughout this chapter draw their own pictures, examine what happens to a few points under the transformations being discussed, and then pass on to the text and exercises.

p. 179 There is no point P for which $l_1 \circ l_2(P) = l_2 \circ l_1(P)$ when the lines l_1 and l_2 are parallel. When, however, the lines intersect there is one such point, the point of intersection.

For any transformation k, say, a point P is called *invariant* if $k(P) = P$. It is readily seen that

    (i) a translation has no invariant point,

    (ii) a rotation has one invariant point, the centre of rotation,

    (iii) a reflection has the points on the line in which the reflection is performed as invariant points.

This is a further significant difference between the three types of isometry.

The fact that $l_1 \circ l_2(P) \neq l_2 \circ l_1(P)$ for any P is qualitatively equivalent to the fact that a translation has no invariant point. The fact that when the lines l_1 and l_2 intersect there is one point P for which $l_1 \circ l_2(P) = l_2 \circ l_1(P)$ corresponds to the fact that a rotation has one invariant point. The connection is not very illuminating.

Exercise 11b Answers

1. The inverse of $l_1 \circ l_2$ is $l_2 \circ l_1$, for

$$(l_2 \circ l_1) \circ (l_1 \circ l_2)(P) = l_2 \circ (l_1 \circ l_1) \circ l_2(P)$$
$$= l_2 \circ l_2(P)$$
$$= P.$$

This corresponds to the statement that, in a general group

$$G = \{g, g', \ldots\}$$

with operation o, that the inverse of $g \circ g'$ is $\tilde{g}' \circ \tilde{g}$.

2. The inverse of $l_1 \circ l_2 \circ l_3$ is $l_3 \circ l_2 \circ l_1$.

3. The centre of rotation is the intersection of the perpendicular bisectors of AA′ and BB′.
Centre of rotation is $(\frac{3}{2}, -\frac{1}{2})$.

4. (a) A′(1, −1), B′(2, −2), C′(−1, −3).
   (b) A″(−1, −1), B″(−2, −2), C″(1, −3).
   (c) The isometry $l_2 \circ l_1$ is a rotation through 180° about the origin.

5. (a) A′(−2, −2), B′(−3, −3), C′(−4, 0).
   (b) A″(·4, −3·2), B″(·2, −4·6), C″(3·2, −3·6).
   (c) The isometry $l_2 \circ l_1$ is a rotation about the point (0, −1), the point of intersection of the two lines. The angle of rotation (approximately 143°) should be compared with the angle between the two lines (approximately $71\frac{1}{2}$°).

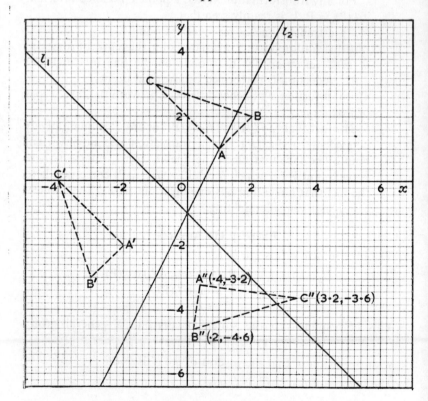

The result of this and the last question should begin to indicate that the combination of two reflections in intersecting lines is a rotation about their point of intersection through twice the angle between them. This result will be discussed in the following text in the Class Book.

6. (a) A'(−2, −2), B'(−3, −3), C'(−4, 0).
   (b) A"(3, 3), B"(4, 4), C"(1, 5).
   (c) The lines l_1 and l_2 are parallel and the combination is a translation through twice the distance ($\sqrt{2}$ units) between the lines, i.e. $2\sqrt{2}$ units 'north-east'.

Although we have chosen what might appear to be special lines in Numbers 5 and 6, this is not in fact the case. The lines are not special for the purpose for which we used them.

* * * * *

p. 180 We consider the image of one point P only and yet are satisfied that we have a general result because the final position P_2 of P can be obtained from P by an isometry which is clearly independent of P: the point O and the angle between the lines are the same whatever P. It is important, however, to decide whether P was, in fact, general enough: we do this in the first question in the following exercise.

Exercise 11c Answers

2. Points in various positions should be considered: for example a point between the lines (not exactly in the middle), a point outside the lines and a point on one of the lines.

3. Q' is the intersection of PS and RP'.

4. l_4 passes through X and is perpendicular to QQ'''.
   Using various points it can also be verified that successive reflections in three parallel lines can be replaced by a single reflection.

   We emphasise again that in all these questions the idea of direct and indirect isometries is very useful. For instance, in Number 2 we know that the result must be a direct isometry, and so we are looking for a translation or rotation (although we do not really know yet that there cannot be other direct isometries, but, in any case, we look first to see if the result is already known), whereas in this question the result must be an indirect isometry and the only one we know so far is a reflection.

5. (a) Reflection in l_A takes points on AC into points on AB, reflection of these in l_K leaves them on AB, and reflection in l_B takes them to points on BC. Thus these three reflections in lines intersecting at K take points on AC into points on BC: by Bachmann's axiom they are equivalent to a reflection in a single line through K. But there is only one reflection which takes points on AC into points on BC: this is reflection in the bisector of angle ACB. Hence the bisector of angle ACB passes through K.

(b) Let the perpendicular bisector of BC be l_A: let the perpendicular bisector of AC be l_B. Let l_A and l_B intersect at K: let KC be l_K. Then if A is reflected successively in l_B, l_K and l_A its image is B. By Bachmann's axiom these three reflections are equivalent to a single reflection in a line through K. But only one reflection takes A into B, that is reflection in the perpendicular bisector of AB: hence the perpendicular bisector of AB passes through K.

Exercise 11d Answers

1. (a) (i) $(0,-1)$ (ii) $(0,0)$ (iii) $(1,-1)$ (iv) $(-1,0)$.

(b) (i) $(1,0)$ (ii) $(0,0)$ (iii) $(1,-1)$ (iv) $(0,1)$.

(c) Reflection is in the line $y = -x$. We thus have (rotation about origin through 90° clockwise) = (reflection in line $y = -x$) o (reflection in x-axis), and we note the (perhaps special) result that the two lines of reflection contain an angle of $45° = \frac{1}{2}(90°)$.

(d) Assuming that $x = 2y$ has been taken the image points are

(i) $(\frac{3}{5},\frac{4}{5})$ (ii) $(0,0)$ (iii) $(\frac{7}{5},\frac{1}{5})$ (iv) $(-\frac{4}{5},\frac{3}{5})$.

The relevant diagram is on the next page.

(e) Reflection is in the line $x + 3y = 0$. We again find that the angle between the reflecting lines is $45° = \frac{1}{2}(90°)$.

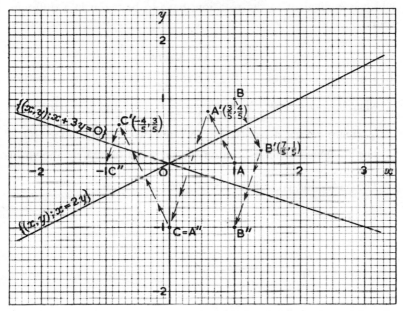

2. The reflections are in any pair of lines through the origin, the angle between them being $22\frac{1}{2}°$. It is not advisable to plot too many points.

3. The reflections are in any pair of lines through the origin, the angle between them being $\frac{\theta}{2}$. In particular $\frac{\theta}{2} = 90°$.

4. The reflections are in any pair of lines through (1,0), the angle between them being 30°; for example the x-axis and the line $\sqrt{3}y + x - 1 = 0$, which is inclined at 150° to the positive x-axis.

The images of the points are

(i) (1,0)   (ii) $\left(\frac{1}{2}, \frac{\sqrt{3}}{2}\right)$ (iii) approximately (1·9,·5)

(iv) approximately (−·4,·5).

It should be noted that in order to obtain an anticlockwise rotation (as opposed to a clockwise rotation) the two lines, reflection in which is equivalent to the rotation, have to be taken in a different order.

Exercise 11e Answers

1. The result of combining the two rotations is not a single rotation when $\theta + \phi = 360°$, for then $\dfrac{\theta}{2} + \dfrac{\phi}{2} = 180°$ and l_1 is parallel to l_2. Hence we get a translation through twice the distance OO_1.

2. The statement is false because the set is not closed, as shown in Number 1.

3. The discussion is similar to that given in the text.

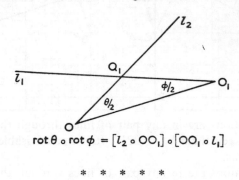

$$\text{rot }\theta \circ \text{rot }\phi = [l_2 \circ OO_1] \circ [OO_1 \circ l_1]$$

*   *   *   *   *

p. 185   As mentioned in the Class Book the next set of exercises gives a variety of results, some of which are fundamental. If time and inclination are available it would be worth working through them all. Many further examples, if required, can be found in the books mentioned in the 'Extra Reading'.

Exercise 11f Answers

1. P can be mapped onto P′ by an isometry in the following ways:

    (i) a reflection in the perpendicular bisector of PP′,

    (ii) a translation through the distance PP′ in the direction P to P′.

    (iii) a rotation about any point O on the perpendicular bisector of PP′ through the angle POP′.

2. (a) Translation determined by PP′ in length and direction, (or a glide reflection which has not yet been mentioned).
   (b) Reflection in the x-axis or a translation determined by PP′ in length and direction.
   (c) Rotation through 180° about point of intersection of PP′ and QQ′.
   (d) Reflection in the line $y = \frac{1}{2}$ or a translation determined by PP′ in length and direction.

3. S′ must lie on the point common to the three circles centres P′, Q′ and R′ of radius SP, SQ and SR respectively. The circles centre P′ and Q′ intersect in two points, if the circle centre R′ were to pass through both these points then R′ would have to lie on P′Q′ which is impossible since we are dealing with a proper triangle. Note that the three circles *must* have a common point because S *has* an image S′.

4. Reflection in the perpendicular bisector of PP′ brings P into coincidence with P′. If now Q is not in coincidence with Q′ then the perpendicular bisector of QQ′ must pass through P′. Hence reflection in this last mentioned line brings Q into coincidence with Q′ without 'separating' P and P′. Finally reflection in P′Q′ must bring R into coincidence with R′ if this has not already been achieved.
   (a) Reflection in P′Q′.
   (b) Reflection in the perpendicular bisector of QQ′ (which must pass through P) followed by reflection in P′Q′: the two reflections are equivalent to a rotation about P through the angle QPQ′.
   (c) In the most complicated possibility, reflection in perpendicular bisector of PP′ followed by a reflection in PP′: the two reflections are equivalent to a rotation about the midpoint of PP′ through 180°.

5. The first thing to notice is that the isometry is indirect and it is therefore likely to be a reflection or something new. In fact it is not a reflection but, for example, could be the combination of a translation and a reflection which cannot be reduced to a single reflection. Such an isometry is called a glide reflection (see

Number 8). One possibility is that the translation maps PQ onto a segment of the x-axis and the reflection is then in the y-axis. The image of the origin is the point $(0, -1)$. (The *same* isometry can be described in many different ways: for example, as a translation specified by PP' followed by reflection in $x = -1$.)

If it is decided to stop here it must be remembered that the glide reflection has not been investigated, and some work must be done on it if it is necessary for examination purposes.

7. (a) $(-1, -1)$ (b) $(0, 0)$ (c) $(0, -1)$ (d) $(-1, 0)$ (e) $(0, -3)$ (f) $(-2, 1)$.

The combination is a glide reflection in the line $y = x$, i.e. a reflection in $y = x$ followed (or preceded by) a translation parallel to $y = x$ through a distance $\sqrt{2}$ units to the left.

8. (a) Equation of l_1' is $y = x$: equation of l_2'' is $y = -x$.
   (b) Since l_2'' and l_3' are parallel, $l_2'' \circ l_3'$ is a translation through twice the distance between them: it is the translation described at the end of the last question.
   (c) The details are clearly similar: but any of these geometrical discussions becomes meaningful only if done by oneself.

9. Suppose that l_1 and l_2 intersect at O and contain an angle θ. Then replace l_1 and l_2 by lines l_1' and l_2' also intersecting at O and containing an angle θ but such that l_1' is parallel to l_3: it follows that l_2' intersects l_1' and l_3 and we are back to the previous case discussed in Numbers 7 and 8.

10. (a) Identity.
    (b) Translation through twice the distance between the lines and perpendicular to them.
    (c) Rotation through twice the angle between the lines about their point of intersection.
    (d) Single reflection in a line through the point of concurrence.
    (e) Single reflection in a line parallel to the three lines.
    (f) Glide reflection.
    (g) Glide reflection.
    (h) Rotation about the point through the sum of the angles of the individual rotations.

(*i*) Rotation if the sum of the angles of the individual rotations is not a multiple of 360°, otherwise a translation.

11. $l_C \circ l_B \circ l_A$ (B) = B. Hence $l_C \circ l_B \circ l_A$ is not a glide reflection, which implies that the three lines are concurrent.

SUGGESTIONS FOR FURTHER WORK

If there is considerable interest one might go on to discuss the group of similarities and the corresponding geometry.

CHAPTER TWELVE

A few Problems on Translations and Rotations

GENERAL NOTES

THIS chapter considers a few problems, many of them 'practical', as opposed to the theoretical problems of the last chapter. The problems explain themselves. The 'Extra Reading' is the same as that given for the previous chapter. Many of the examples are modified from Yaglom's book, which contains a mass of useful material.

NOTES ON TEXT OF CLASS BOOK
AND ANSWERS TO EXERCISES

pp. 190–191 The group properties which we use in this question are the existence of an identity and that for any translation there exists an inverse translation. This sounds a trivial statement, but whenever an inverse exists the statement must perforce be trivial; nevertheless, the statement should be made in order to emphasise that this seemingly particular problem illustrates our central mathematical concepts of structure.

As for the rest of the problem we are, in fact, trying to find the appropriate representative of an equivalence class. The equivalence class is the set of all line-segments 30 metres long in the direction 20° east of north. The whole equivalence class may be identified with the translation which transforms every point a distance 30 metres in a direction N 20° E. (In fact, as we shall see in Book 5, it is more usual to call this equivalence class a *vector*, but the addition of vectors is isomorphic to the combination of translations, hence the identification. Many of the problems discussed here are often discussed in terms of vectors: there is no difference.) An appropriate representative of this equivalence class would be a line-segment which had one end point on the circle centre P and the other on the circle centre Q. Sometimes there are several appropriate representatives, sometimes one, sometimes none.

pp. 192–193 The canal problem can also be analysed as above: in the first place we have a translation determined by PQ and we are looking for three translations whose combination is the given one. One of these three translations is determined by the fact that we have to cross the canal at right angles. Since the combination of translations is associative and commutative we can take this translation first and choose a representative line-segment which starts at P, and so on.

This problem could be solved by the methods of the calculus for dealing with maxima and minima discussed in Book 5, but this method proves unnecessarily awkward.

Exercise 12a Answers

1. Possible answers are
   (a) PQ of length 67·5 m, bearing of Q from P N 50° E, circle centre P radius 10 m, circle centre Q radius 10 m, XY of length 30 m and the bearing of Y from X N 50° E.
   (b) PQ and XY as in (a), circle centre P radius 17·5 m and circle centre Q radius 20 m.
   (c) PQ of length 30 m, the rest as in (a).

The answers to the following exercises are given approximately to correspond to the pupil's scale drawing. They can, of course, be calculated exactly. We shall develop some of the results necessary for this in Book 5.

For Answer 2, see next page.

2. Length of the shortest route is approximately 5·4 in.

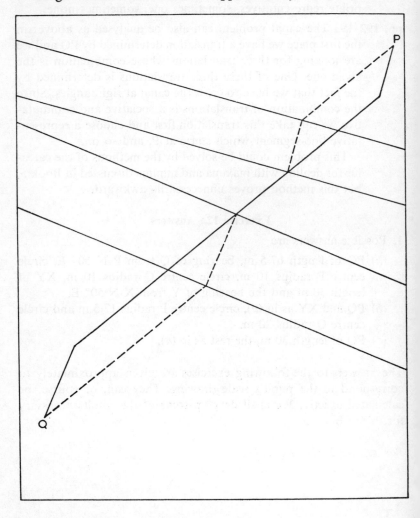

3. (a) Ground speed ≏ 395 m.p.h., track ≏ 013°.

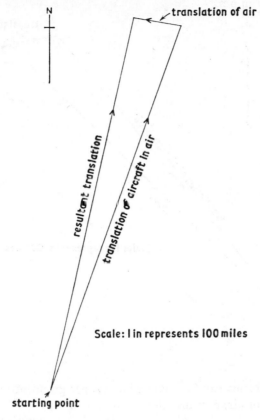

N

translation of air

resultant translation

translation of aircraft in air

Scale: 1 in represents 100 miles

starting point

For Answer 3(b), see next page.

(b) Aircraft's nose pointed in direction ≏ 220°, ground speed ≏ 437 m.p.h.

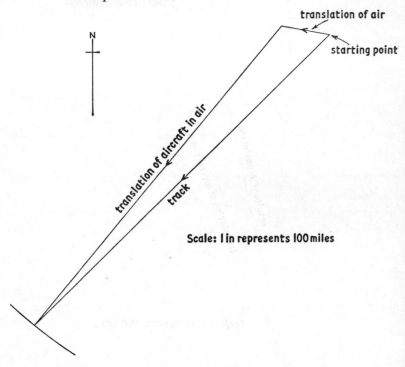

Scale: I in represents 100 miles

These problems can be analysed as proper group problems:

(translation of air) o (translation of aircraft in air)

= translation relative to ground.

Thus in part (a) where we know (translation of aircraft in air) and (translation of air), we have merely to form their combination in order to find the ground translation. Since the combination of translations is commutative we can combine in any order. Choose any point P as the starting point, transform it under one translation and then transform the result under the other translation obtaining a point P″. PP″ represents the resulting single translation in magnitude and direction.

In the diagram we represent the translations effected in one hour.

Part (*b*) is a little more complicated for the only translation we know completely is the translation of the air. So if we perform this translation first and it maps a point P onto a point P' then we know that the translation of the aircraft in the air maps P' onto some point P'' on the circle radius 4 in (on the scale drawing) centre P'. On the other hand P'' must also be the image of P under the translation relative to the ground and we know the direction of this (i.e. the track). Hence if we draw a line through P in the direction of the track, P'' will be the point of intersection (if any) of this line with the circle centre P'.

4. (*a*)

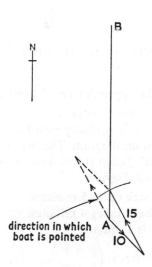

Scale: ½ in represents 10 miles

Direction in which boat is pointing ≃ 330°.
(*b*) Journey takes approximately 6½ hours.

For Answer 4(c), see next page.

(c)

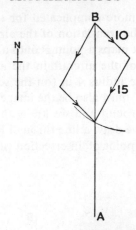

Scale: $\frac{1}{2}$ in represents 10 miles

Direction $\simeq 208°$.

(d) Journey will take approximately 2 hours.

Note: Our diagrams show 'distances in one hour' and 'distances', both to the same scale. It is perfectly possible, of course, to use two different scales on the same diagram. The two scales are then, clearly, 'velocity' and 'distance'. When the diagram shows velocities only it is often called a *velocity diagram*.

5. From A to B and back takes 5 minutes.
   From A to C and back takes 4 minutes.
   Difference in times is 1 minute.

6. Representation of $t_1 \circ t_2$ is $\begin{pmatrix} p + p' \\ q + q' \end{pmatrix}$.

7. (a) $\begin{pmatrix} -9 \\ -5 \end{pmatrix}$ (b) $\begin{pmatrix} -5 \\ 7 \end{pmatrix}$ (c) $\begin{pmatrix} 28 \\ 21 \end{pmatrix}$.

* * * * * *

pp. 196 et seq. The problem discussed has a complicated appearance and should be taken in easy stages. A thorough discussion of this problem should teach the pupil all that he is ever likely to wish to know about the combination of rotations and the constructions therein involved.

As verified in the previous chapter the combination of two rotations is a rotation, unless the sum of the angles of rotation is 360°. Therefore, the combination of the three rotations given in the text is a rotation and since BP maps onto BP''', B is an invariant point of this rotation and hence must be its centre. Therefore, an alternative method of finding B would be to do the construction necessary to find the centre of rotation of the combination of successive rotations. The details of this construction are implicit in the discussion of this sort of combination given in the previous chapter: i.e. replace each rotation by two reflections, one reflection being in the line of centres.

Incidentally, we see that if in a problem like the one discussed in the text the sum of the angles of rotation is 360° or a multiple of 360°, then the resulting combination of rotations is a translation, and hence there is no invariant point B: the problem then has no solution, in general. In the very special case when the translation is the identity there are, of course, any number of solutions.

p. 196 A, B and C are the points whose co-ordinates are approximately (40,30), (20,40) and (15,25).

p. 197 The figure of the complete construction should only be used when the pupil has already started to make his own drawing and needs some guidance. It is very doubtful if anything can be learned by merely looking at the finished figure.

Exercise 12b Answers

1. The combination of the three rotations is a rotation through 180°, i.e. a half-turn. It follows that the centre of rotation is the midpoint of PP''' and we need no further point Q.
The vertices of the triangle are (5,40), (38,28) and (30,50).

2. A (20,5)   B(45,30)   C (45,50)   D (25,30).

3. Pupils should realise that the result is a translation. It is of approximately 35·3 units in a direction at approximately 52° to the positive x-axis.

4. The result is, of course, a rotation. The centre of rotation has approximate co-ordinates (37,37) and the angle of rotation is 150°.

MISCELLANEOUS EXERCISES V Answers

1. (a) True   (b) False   (c) True   (d) This could be true if
   for instance angle $A = \dfrac{\pi}{2}$, then BA' would be parallel to AC.

2. (i) £3 0s 11d   (ii) $3(x - 3)(4x + 5)$ (iii) 7·38 cm.

3. (i) $2\frac{1}{2}$ (ii) $11\frac{7}{8}$ mph.

4. (i) (a) 230   (b) 64   (c) 204   (ii) 23; 212.

5. (i) £4 4s 9d   (ii) £43 17s 4d   (iii) 3281 ft.

6. (a) $t = c - \dfrac{b}{a - 2}$ (b) $\dfrac{tx}{x + y}$ (c) ·2885.

7. (a) $-1·27, ·47$ (b) 1.

8. (a) $\simeq 2·37$ (b) RS, $9\frac{3}{13}$ cm.

9. 25%, 12%, 25%, 38%, 15%, 60%, 25%.

10. The numbers in A, B and C are of the form $3k + 1, 3l + 2, 3m$,
    where k, l and m are integers. Hence $a + b$ is of the form
    $3(k + l) + 3$ and belongs to C. Similarly $ab \in B$, $a + c \in A$,
    $b + c \in B$ and $bc \in C$.

11. $3x + y \leqslant 240, x + 3y \leqslant 120; x = 75, y = 15$; maximum profit
    £1 6s 3d.

12. £2029 1s 0d; £45 19s 0d.

13. (a) 82°   (b) 5 cm, 35 sq cm   (c) 84°.

14. (a) 3 in   (b) $P = 6\sqrt{x} + \dfrac{1}{\sqrt{x}}$.

15. (a) $-0·89$ to $3·39$ (b) $-0·56$ to $3·56$.

16. Median £107 m, mean £102 m, variance £157·3 m.

17.

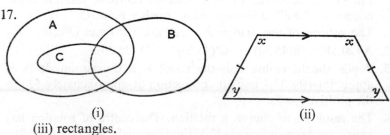

(i)   (ii)

(iii) rectangles.

18. (i) 10   (ii) A possible flow diagram is given below.

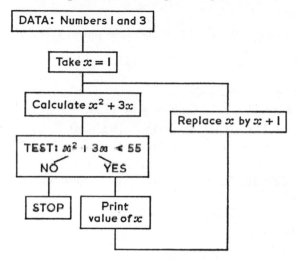

The corresponding programme would be

READ DATA $1 \rightarrow x_1$
$3 \rightarrow x_2$

FOLLOW INSTRUCTIONS

1. $x_1 \rightarrow x_3$
2. $x_3 \times x_3 \rightarrow x_4$
3. $x_2 \times x_3 \rightarrow x_5$
4. $x_4 + x_5 \rightarrow x_4$
5. TEST If $x_4 < 55$ JUMP to 7
6. OFF
7. Print x_3
8. $x_1 + x_3 \rightarrow x_3$
9. JUMP to 2.

19.

No. of faces showing	0	1	2	3
No. of cubes	216	216	72	8

20. (i) 8   (ii) $-1\frac{1}{2}$ (iii) 64.

21. From $-1\cdot32$ to $0\cdot57$.

22. Wind from $049°\ 4'$ or $130°\ 56'$; 2.40 pm or 1.29·5 pm

23. (a) $\begin{pmatrix} 3 & -5 \\ -4 & 7 \end{pmatrix}$; $x = -11$, $y = 15$.

24. (i) 4 sq in   (ii) 8 in.

25. (i) 18 cm, 80 cm   (ii) 3 in, 4 in, 12 in.

26. (i) $(a - 15)(a + 14)$ (ii) $(x - 1)(p - q)$
    (iii) $(3 + x - y)(3 - x + y)$

27. $1000a + 100b + 10c + d$; $1000d + 100c + 10b + a$.
    The difference is $999a + 90b - 90c - 999d$, which is divisible by 9.
    With $b = c$ the difference is $999(a - d)$, which is divisible by 9 and 37.

28. $x = \dfrac{49}{500}$, $y = \dfrac{1}{10}$; two yards start.

29. A glide reflection in $y = 3$ of 6 units in the direction of the positive x-axis.
    A′(0,1)   B′(-2,1)   C′(0,3).
    A glide reflection in $y = x - 2$ of $6\sqrt{2}$ units.

31. (i) 16 sq in   (ii) AD $= \sqrt{17}$ in $\simeq 4\cdot123$ in
    (iii) $\tan^{-1}\frac{4}{3} \simeq 53°\ 8'$.

32. $a = \cdot006$, $b = 3$.

W	100	200	300	400	500
Efficiency	22·2	38·1	50	59·3	66·7

33. Height = 3·64 in.

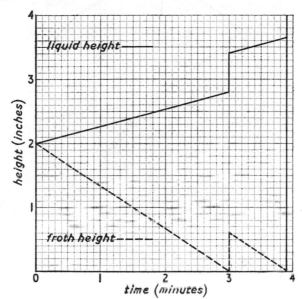

34. (a) $(a + b)(a - b)(a^2 + b^2)$.
    (b) $k = 12$.
    (c) (i) x^6 (ii) $y^{\frac{3}{2}}$ (iii) z^8.

35. Total time $= \dfrac{300x - 1800}{x(x - 15)}$ hours.

Average speed $= \dfrac{x(x - 15)}{x - 6}$ mph, $x = 60$.

36.

Subject	Angle on Pie Chart
English	$100°$
Mathematics	$87\frac{1}{2}°$
French	$80°$
Geography	$55°$
History	$37\frac{1}{2}°$

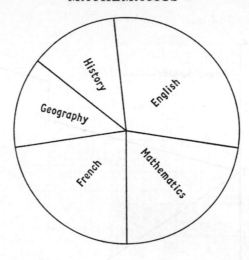

37. (i) $b^2 - 4ac \geqslant 0$.

If $\dfrac{x^2 - 15}{2x - 8} = k$ then the condition for real x gives

$(k - 5)(k - 3) > 0$, i.e. the required result.

(ii) $4y^2 - 65y + 16 = 0$; $y = \frac{1}{4}$ or 16; $x = -1$ or 2.

38. 4 days in every 13.

39. Let the image of B under reflection in the power line be B'. Then AB' cuts the power line at the required point X.

40. □ is not distributive over o. (Satisfactory justification could be given by displaying a counter-example, e.g.

$$b \, \square \, (b \, \text{o} \, b) \neq (b \, \square \, b) \, \text{o} \, (b \, \square \, b)$$

or by stating the known fact that a set cannot display group structure for each of two operations, one of which is distributive over the other.)